Modern Sex Techniques

Modern Sex Techniques

by

Robert Street

Illustrated

ARCHER HOUSE, INC., NEW YORK

DISTRIBUTED BY HERMAN & STEPHENS, INC.

MANUFACTURED IN THE UNITED STATES OF AMERICA
BY GANIS & HARRIS, NEW YORK

Contents

and female contrasted—The wife a source of sexual disappointment—The danger of self modesty—A husband's responsibility—The importance of discussion—A suggested approach—Women sexually apathetic—How to discourage apathy—The lack of sexual honesty—Its affect upon a wife—The importance of proper conditioning—The danger of bad breath

Introduction

NOT so long ago, the British Bar Association admitted that the principal factor responsible for English divorces is sexual incompatibility. The Association is to be praised for having undertaken an analysis of the unfortunate and important divorce problem and for having made public its findings. There is no doubt in the author's mind that similar studies made in other countries would result in like conclusions; sex is governed and controlled by a natural and universal law which is common to all individuals, and all persons are subject to its influence in greater or lesser degree.

Whether one cares to admit it or not, it is a fundamental and vital force in preserving the home and family. Its destructive effect upon marriage results primarily from the fact that proper sexual procedure is taken for granted, that it is regarded as an uncomplicated phenomenon. This has tended to breed ignorance injurious to the permanency of marriage and has marred the future happiness of many women.

If this thesis be accepted, then the vital problem which it poses must be solved through intelligent, practical, codified, and instructive discussion capable of being understood and followed by the layman with beneficial results.

The purpose of this book, then, is to concentrate on the subject of sex, to do it with unprecedented and yet unoffensive frankness that leaves nothing for imaginative guess-work, and to take up the matter where previous treatments leave it. Its motives are simple: to enlighten and protect the innocent, further to educate the experienced, to adjust the sexually incompatible, and to strengthen the foundation of the home. It emphasizes the problems faced by women only because they are the principal sufferers of their own and man's sexual ignorance.

Few mothers possess sufficient experience or a taste for the type of frankness necessary to impart adequate sexual knowledge to their daughters. Few fathers are qualified to advise their offspring, because the average man boasts of a far broader pre-marital sex life than he has actually experienced, and his wild oats have been sown largely in the fields of his imagination.

It is little to be wondered, then, that with generation following generation, this situation fails to improve and, if anything, grows considerably worse, as our increasing divorce rate testifies.

Even assuming that both parents are sufficiently informed, the problem of educating the child usually remains insurmountable: to impart a complete knowledge of the subject is a task which grates upon the delicate sensibilities of the average father and mother. It becomes almost impossible when a widow is confronted with an adolescent son, or a widower with his growing daughter, especially when the children are rapidly approaching the age for matrimony.

Many parents will immediately protest the validity of these assertions and will claim to have educated their children effectively by following the formulas laid down by competent authority. Such contentions are very seldom reliable, because parents themselves are usually ill-informed and because it is invariably impracticable for those occupying a parental relationship to tell the child everything he or she should know. Such explanations poorly made by parents can definitely shock the adolescent mind; complete frankness implies a discussion of the details of personal sex experience which few parents can bring themselves to undertake even on the eve of a child's marriage.

It must be emphasized here that such intimate revelations by parents may, to a son or daughter, take on a character of indecency which does not exist when coming from a third person. Many readers will recall their discomfiture when, as children, they first fully realized that childbirth was the result of intercourse between their parents. While admitting that other persons may engage in such practices, most children reject the thought that their own fathers and mothers have similarly indulged themselves.

However, this is only the most prominently emphasized phase of the broad cycle of behavior involved in our physical relationships. Suppose that a child who has just become aware of his parents' sexual activity were called upon to ponder over the additional knowledge of the more intimate preliminaries to intercourse. Such added awareness could result only in absolute incredulity and disgust. Nevertheless, the child, particularly a daughter, should be acquainted with the varied forms of perfectly normal sexual outlet to which he or she may be introduced on the nuptial night. With respect to the girl, a definite knowledge of normal sexual practices may prevent her from regarding her newly acquired mate as a loathsome degenerate.

Actually, it is far better for a child to acquire intimate information of this character from a text, from something with which he or she has a purely impersonal relationship. Only in this manner can maturing children be brought to realize that those who indulge in sexual activity are normal human beings engaging in a perfectly normal function.

This volume is designed, among other objectives, to achieve this purpose. Even parents with the proper ability and background find that propriety alone will not allow them to touch upon the vast variety of intimate and vital information which everyone should have but very few possess. There is, in addition, a broader field of knowledge which parents must have if they are adequately to protect their maturing children.

This is not to imply, of course, that parents should ignore the problems and questions of their children when they come directly for information, or that they should always be referred to a book dealing with the subject. These matters in which a child approaches his father or mother are usually not complicated, are easily disposed of, and do not involve a complete exposure of the adult's sex life. An individual of normal intelligence can perceive immediately to what extent he may become involved and whether he will be forced beyond his limitations. Furthermore, when the adolescent reaches the point where he or she voluntarily seeks specific information of the parent, it is certain that the child has already acquired a sufficient background from outside sources to be ready to absorb a more explicit, accurate, and advanced account of the subject.

These pages contain none of the customary and conventional superficialities and generalities which have been endlessly repeated and paraphrased. They consider only perfectly normal people, usual situations, and constant factors. Neither does this book discuss abnormalities of any kind, either in practice or among individuals. Such exceptions to natural behavior, although they appear numerous when taken collectively, are, nevertheless, minor when compared with the preponderantly normal. The possibility that the average family will be touched by these exceptions is too remote to be considered, and there is little to be gained from such a secondary discussion.

Nor is this a tome on biology or physiology, purporting to be a commentary on sexual problems but instead embodying chapters on the development of the fetus, pages on inconsequential anatomy, and a comparatively few lines on the vital aspects of sexual procedure. Only such sketches as are absolutely necessary for a proper consideration of the matter herein discussed are included, and they are few in number. It might be emphasized, also, that, regardless of the page length of any previous works on the subject of sexology, few, *if any,* when robbed of the supporting amount of material *entirely irrelevant* to the sex act, will contain a discussion of practical matters—matters in which the layman is chiefly interested—that compares in size with the pertinent detail and coverage of this volume. Therein lies its unique value.

This text, then, is to be regarded essentially as an instrument the purpose of which is to relieve one of the major threats to the stability of the home: sexual incompatibility. In a world of chaos and in an era in which national and international integrity have fallen to a low level, there remains only the solid structure of the home to form the basis for a re-establishment of the ancient standards of virtue.

Any contribution which may cement the husband-and-wife or father-and-mother relationship and which will interfere with the constant grinding of the divorce mill, should be valuable, since a separation of the marital ties encourages looseness, and looseness leads to a complete breakdown of moral fiber. Ironically, a dissolution of the marriage vows is too frequently unnecessary, and an early understanding of the sex problem would eliminate the one outstanding factor that eventually contributes to a parting of the ways.

Robert Street

Modern Sex Techniques

1.

Initial Intercourse

A GREAT deal has been written on the subject of this
chapter, most of which has had little purpose other
than to attract the lascivious. Where a writer is really sincere in his effort to deal with the problem, the treatment
is often sketchy in that too great a neglect of necessary
detail exists and that too much emphasis is laid on the
theme, "Be tender, be understanding."

It would be interesting to see a man, though he be in
every respect a barbarian, who on the bridal night at least
does not possess tender emotions for his wife. His subsequent offenses may be characterized by ignorance and the
inability to control himself, but never by a desire to be
brutal. From a woman's point of view, if her husband exhibits complete ignorance of how to go about a delicate
matter and lacks self-control once he is aroused, any tenderness on his part must become of secondary importance.

It is probable that much of the carelessness concerning
the duties of the male on the bridal night and the honeymoon is due to the attitude that nature has allowed for this
procedure in her plans; that she does not regard it as a
particularly delicate or difficult operation, and will automatically protect the fool from his folly in this one respect
at least. To a limited extent, this philosophy is valid.

Certainly, intercourse appears to be a perfectly normal
function, performed as easily and successfully by the sav-

age as by the civilized and with no apparent disturbing after-effects. It must, therefore, be a very simple procedure and one requiring no particular knowledge. In the view of many, the pain of initial intercourse, like the pains of labor, is something to which a woman must reconcile herself.

For the state of labor, however, nature has also provided for the automatic delivery of the infant; throughout a large portion of the world, this process is aided only by a mid-wife. In our more civilized society, even police officers have performed with passable competence in an emergency. Yet, what civilized man in this country would consider allowing his wife to pass through childbirth without the attendance of a qualified doctor?

Apparently, what is good enough for the savage and for us in one instance, is good enough only for the savage in another. However, in initial intercourse women have hemorrhaged to death, although such an occurrence is very rare. In view of even so remote a possibility, it is strange that the situation is too frequently accepted as something about which the layman needs not a particle of knowledge.

Of course, almost every man who has had the experience of marrying a woman possessing a hymen manages to survive the ordeal somehow, just as a man who has never delivered an extemporaneous address finally stumbles through an unorganized presentation. Undoubtedly, nature has done her best to provide against physical, if not psychological, damage, and has been more or less successful. As with everything in life, however, the scientific approach is preferable, even on principle alone. Let us, therefore, analyze the problem.

Behavior on the marriage night may vary according to the conditions which exist. There is no one, stipulated, undeviating procedure which can be laid down as a universal law, because, naturally, consideration depends entirely upon the physical structure of the bride: Whether she be a virgin, or whether she has had marital or premarital experience. In the two latter instances, the bridegroom faces no insurmountable physical difficulties.

Of course, there are certain fundamentals which do not change, either on the bridal night or subsequently; of these, self-control and leisurely preliminary sex play are the most important. However, with respect to the specific problem of the virgin, which is what primarily occupies us here, there can be and are varying circumstances which determine male behavior. Let us deal with this outworn concept of the hymen and its relationship to various suppositions as to what constitutes chastity.

It stands to reason that pure chastity is a matter of thought as well as of behavior. If we limit our discussion to fundamental physical qualifications, many persons conclude that an undoubted virgin is one who approaches her wedding night thoroughly intact.

Should a man be one of those individuals who appraises morals exclusively on the existence of a more or less tough section of membrane barring entrance to the vagina, he may be satisfied if it is present. But he may be completely deceived by either its presence or its absence, because an intact hymen is proof of only one thing: that it has not been ruptured. Its existence cannot, by any stretch of the imagination, mean that a woman has participated in no form of sex indulgence. In many cases a male has partly entered the vaginal canal, merely stretching the hymen, but not breaking it.

Furthermore, any number of girls will allow every form of intimacy short of actual intercourse. By this it is not meant that intercourse with them is impossible, but only that such a girl always exacts promises that her partner omit the final phase of the relationship. However. the male can experience orgasm and even induce one in his partner, since he has only to move his penis along the external genitals, brushing the clitoris. In fact, this a frequent variation in instances where women of low sensitivity experience no sensation about the vagina, but are more aroused when the male organ rather than the finger induces the sex sensation at the clitoris. Obviously, a woman who maintains her hymen intact under such conditions can hardly be considered as retaining a virginal status. Certainly, even lesser intimacies must be regarded as modifying a woman's virginity.

On the other hand, is the absence of the maidenhead in itself any indication that a woman has been violated? No more so than its presence proves virginity. It is not necessary to seek far for the reason. The hymen may have been accidentally ruptured in childhood or adolescence in ways too numerous to list, and a girl may not have the slightest awareness of the occurrence. Nevertheless, she is as virginal as her sister whose hymen has remained intact.

But what if the hymen is not lacking by reason of accident but has been lost in the routine of sex practice? Is it possible to determine the one from the other? The answer to that is that it depends entirely upon the structure of the girl, on how capable an actress she may be, and on the male's gullibility. If she has a small canal, can lie plausibly, and is able to affect a realistic simulation of pain, she can stage a most convincing performance and completely mislead a spouse who understandably indulges in wishful thinking. In many circumstances, even a physician can be deceived.

Thus, as a practical matter, the absence of the hymen is

no guide to the virginity of a woman, nor is virginity a standard by which to evaluate chastity. Where, then, do we stand? The truth is, we stand exactly where we should. A woman should be taken on trust and trust alone, just as she accepts a man; if he is not sufficiently tolerant for that, then he should remain a bachelor. It will be best for both, and certainly best for a woman; otherwise, she will lead a life of continuous torment.

There is no fixed law for determining the future morality of one's wife. We must rely on the estimate we have made of her as a person. The fact that she is intact on her wedding night is no guarantee that she will not slip from her pedestal five years hence. Nor is the fact that she may have been indifferent to conventions prior to her marriage any indication that she will not make a constant and devoted mate. A woman's chastity depends upon too many influences, the least important of which is her self-control and the most important of which is opportunity.

Let us assume, however, that the groom will rejoice in the discovery that his wife is intact on the bridal night. If he is interested in approaching this occasion with a certain amount of security, he can gain it by following certain procedures. Similar knowledge need not overburden the prospective bride. Since it is she who will bear what inconvenience there is, she can relieve it by co-operation.

At the outset, it is well for a woman to understand that the rupturing of the hymen is not necessarily an excrutiatingly painful experience. Normally, if it is done properly, there exists what may be described as a painful moment following which there is immediate relief. There is nothing about the entire operation to fear or dread. In fact, many women experience no pain at all. A definite and somewhat severe tenderness does continue in many cases, however, for a number of days following, but it is in no wise so disturbing as to confine a woman to bed and so easily bearable that she need feel no concern.

However, there do exist conditions with which the male should be acquainted and which will have a bearing on his behavior. The hymen membrane varies in toughness; if it fails to yield quickly under reasonable pressure, it is obviously wise to attempt to weaken it by gradual stretching and not to insist upon completing the process on the wedding night. Should repeated failures occur, the matter should be referred to a physician, who will determine the difficulty and relieve it. Usually this involves only a simple and relatively painless puncture of the hymen.

It is also intelligent for the prospective bride, when she appears for the Wassermann test, which most states now prescribe, to undergo a thorough physical examination, learn whether her proportions are large or small, and ask her doctor's advice. She should then discuss her physical condition with her future husband.

This, perhaps, is most important of all and should be constantly carried in mind by the groom: All initiative, all control lies completely within his hands. The bride can do only one thing of importance, and that is to relax. Even so, the husband must repeatedly remind her of this and assist her in it.

Before attempting intercouse, the husband should also thoroughly acquaint himself with the genital region of his wife. He should direct his attention to the construction of the vaginal canal and the location of the hymen, so that direct and not angular pressure may be used against it. Depending upon height and size, it may be necessary for a woman to be placed with her buttocks on a pillow to elevate the extremities, or she may be forced to bend her knees sharply, or even wrap her legs about the waist of the male, to mention only a few considerations. These are physical peculiarities which the male must study and about which the physical examination mentioned can be most helpful; women very definitely vary in structure.

The correct angle of entrance is not at all important in subsequent intercourse once the vaginal section has accustomed itself to accomodate the male organ; the walls of the vaginal canal automatically adjust the penis to a comfortable position. However, for the single purpose of rupturing the hymen, a direct and not angular pressure simplifies the process, and this requires a certain familiarity with female structure.

It is probable that not one man in ten, prior to marriage or subsequent to it, can draw a simple sketch of the cross section of a woman's genitals to include the uterus, the outer lips, the clitoris, the urethra, the inner lips, the vaginal muscles, the hymen, the vaginal canal, and the tip of the womb—just eight small parts and seven of them all-important to an adequate understanding of what is involved in proper sex indulgence, and ignorance of which may interfere with enjoyment. Such a sketch is presented on the next page. It should be studied; on the bridal night, instead of making a determined effort to rupture the hymen at all costs, the husband should compare the diagram with his wife's genital region, as determined by actual examination. The approach to this matter should be casual and delicate to avoid giving a bride the impression that this investigation arises from pure physical lust, and to avoid arousing the suspicion that the husband may be unconventional in his habits. If one goes about this properly, he will also go a long way toward destroying future inhibitions which may lead to false modesty. A study of the sketch, if it does nothing else, may prevent a blundering groom from battering away at the tip of the womb in subsequent intercourses.

Once the hymen has been ruptured with only normal strain, it will in most cases, hemorrhage. It should then be allowed to bleed itself out, provided, of course, the flow

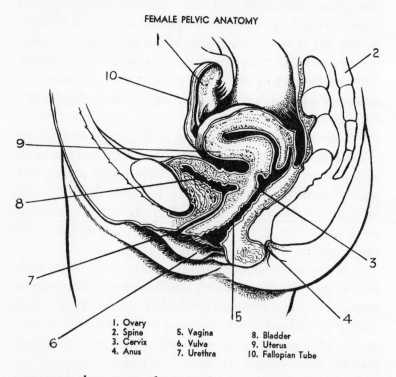

FEMALE PELVIC ANATOMY

1. Ovary
2. Spine
3. Cervix
4. Anus
5. Vagina
6. Vulva
7. Urethra
8. Bladder
9. Uterus
10. Fallopian Tube

appears to be a normal one and ceases within a reasonable length of time. Actually, that is sufficient progress for one night, and a thoughtful husband will so regard it. He may be sure, also, that his wife will not be too opposed to a cessation of activity, and he should not be misled by any protestation that she is willing to proceed. She may do so only because she feels that an interruption interferes with the satisfaction of his passion. She realizes that this is a disagreeable performance and is moved by a feeling of guilt.

Actually, this is the true situation; she has been tense and anxious, and certainly with ample reason. She has been expecting a somewhat painful and generally disagreeable experience, and her nerves are as taut as those of a patient in a dentist's chair. Furthermore, it is completely out of the question for men or women to give their best to sex indulgence unless they are thoroughly relaxed. This is particularly true of a woman. It is abnormal to force upon her something which she is neither physically nor mentally adjusted to meet. If one still feels amative, there are ways to spend the time, ways so obvious that they require no explanation. A virgin awaits introductions to the world of sex. A perfect lover with the proper understanding will control his own passion on this particular night as he will do frequently in the future and, following the rupture, will devote himself exclusively to relaxing her and not himself.

If hemorrhages occur on subsequent attempts, the male should restrain his impulses until bleeding stops permanently. Common sense suggests that where a bleeding occurs, irritation is present. No man would apply friction to an open wound on his own body, and he must be equally considerate with his wife.

For the next few occasions following the stoppage of the flow, the introduction of the male organ into the vagina should, if necessary, be a gradual one; only an indifferent groom will insist on entering beyond an inch after the first signal of female discomfort. There should be no attempt to penetrate the full distance under any circumstances until the depth and width of the canal have been ascertained. It is possible that the woman may be so constructed as to be at all times "tight," as the expression goes, and to have a short canal. It is astonishing how the length and width of the canal can vary with women and affect the pleasure of intercourse from the purely physical standpoint. The male should try to estimate these dimensions by inserting a well lubricated finger to the cervix in the vaginal vault. This will give him an approximation of size.

Returning to the actual introduction of the penis, the groom should withdraw at the first sign of female distress, and repeat the procedure several times until easy access to the distance of an inch is permitted with lessening discomfort. That is sufficient for this particular period also; it might be added that during these invasions the male organ should be well lubricated with vaseline or, preferably, surgical jelly.

Upon succeeding occasions, penetration may be increased bit by bit, thus allowing the vaginal walls sufficient opportunity to become used to this gradual crowding. After several periods of careful and considerate conditioning, it will be found that, outside of a sharp but temporary twinge of sensitivity immediately upon distending the mouth of the vagina, entrance can be effected without difficulty; one is then, and only then, ready to undertake the problem of perfect intercourse. This cannot be accomplished overnight, and it is dealt with in subsequent chapters.

It must be emphasized that the depth of the vagina and vaginal vault varies with different women. Even upon their fullest expansion they may not, perhaps for several months, be able to accommodate more than half to three-quarters of the male organ. A great many women, prior to childbirth and in numerous instances following, never stretch in depth to a point where they can accept the full length of an erected penis, especially if the male organ is larger than average. The genitals of men, as well as those of women, vary in proportions, and a normal male penis may have an erected length varying from five to seven inches.

In these situations, it is unwise to batter as with a ram upon the vaginal vault and the tip of the womb. Eventually this will create pain and tenderness, and accomplish nothing other than to develop in the wife an aversion to the sex act. It is very probable that childbirth will ultimately make an adjustment in size.

The intelligent and considerate groom will devote a week or ten days to gradually introducing his bride to the delightful world of sex instead of trying to bring it about in one operation. When he feels that he has fully accomplished this to the best of his ability, he should see that she is examined by a physician to make absolutely certain that no injury has occurred, especially if the wife experiences any constant pain during relationships. She will then probably never have reason to find sex repugnant as a consequence of blunders on the honeymoon.

Unfortunately, and in spite of all that may be said, many women will find the bridal night extremely disagreeable. Normal men exist who when sexually aroused have no control whatever over their impulses. They become, literally, frenzied and oblivious to everything but their own needs. A wife's discomfort cannot even register, so overwhelmed is this type by its own emotion and so driven to satisfy it.

There is little a woman can do under the circumstances. She can submit and hope that time will either condition her to these assaults or that her husband will eventually introduce reason into his approach, a most unlikely probability. Her safest course is to have an immediate showdown. Regardless of the honeymoon stage, she must make it firmly understood that, under no circumstances, will she submit to further attacks of that nature. She must strongly impress upon him that his emotion is no excuse for rape, because rape it is. She must warn him that unless he exerts an intelligent control over his future behavior, she will forbid intimacy. And she must mean it.

A man of this type is a bully by nature, and like all bullies is quick to seize upon any physical advantage he possesses. Once a woman submits to his indifferent handling of her, she becomes from that moment a piece of sexual apparatus to be used and abused according to his inclinations. Unless she faces the situation squarely and at once, her general future with such a husband is already forecast.

If one accepts the accounts of women who have described the events of the bridal night and those immediately following, a thoughtful husband will realize how easy it is to make mistakes. The problem must be approached leisurely; it must be considered studiously; and it must be treated practically. It is not a glamorous or routine undertaking, but a very serious one. In fact, the bridal night should be regarded not as an appropriate occasion for the enjoyment of intercourse, but as the most unsuitable time for it.

2.

Adult Sexual Behavior

MOST women have the mistaken idea that the sexual nature of all normal females is relatively the same as their own. They have heard or have read of the highly passionate type and have assumed, by relying on gossip or the treatment of sex in romantic novels, that the phrase "highly passionate" describes a woman who is something of a rarity and above normal in her emotions. This, of course, is not true. If a woman is correctly described as "over passionate," we may consider her abnormal; the word "over" indicates that she is beyond the border line. The word "highly," however, has its own meaning, and is employed to describe a woman who is unusually passionate but not abnormally so. It must be remembered, also, that what the inexperienced may regard as unusual, the experienced look upon as quite ordinary.

Consequently, the most that can be assumed of a woman who is correctly referred to as "highly passionate" is that she comprises a member of the minority. But minorities can vary in size, and such a woman is the member of a very large minority, constituting perhaps, thirty to forty per cent of all normally sexed women; the rest are below her in the emotional scale, but also well within the confines of normalcy.

Since "frigidity" and "nymphomania" can be regarded as outside the boundaries of normalcy, it is clear that there is a large range in between where the behavior of women may vary considerably and still fall within the limits of normalcy. This chapter and the five following are, perhaps, the most important in the book, because an understanding of them will enable a woman to suspect her sexual possibilities, enlighten her and her husband as to how she may be more properly accommodated, and enable her to grasp what is probably the basis of much unrealized sexual dissatisfaction and general irritability. It will also suggest to the husband the possibility that he may be neglecting to fulfill the sexual requirements of his wife or develop her capacities to their fullest extent.

Because it is impossible to know with certainty the precise manner in which to treat a delicate problem unless a similar one has been handled successfully in the past, no man of limited experience or of unobserving habits has the ability to recognize the peculiarities which distinguish one woman from another and to treat her in the manner suitable to her nature. Nor is it expected that every normal man will have either the opportunity or the desire to associate with a variety of women and, through repeated contact, come to recognize the temperament of every individual woman.

Consequently, a husband with limited pre-marital associations who may have had, by coincidence, relationships only with women of high emotional levels, may regard a wife who is more reserved and subdued in her passion as bordering on frigidity; whereas, in fact, such a woman, if properly conditioned, may in other respects be every bit as passionate as the easily aroused. Unfortunately, the husband, being unaware of this and judging all women by his limited experience, will, unless otherwise informed, be dissatisfied with his marital sex life, while his wife, though ignorant of the reason, knows only that sex relationships leave her disturbed or else completely indifferent. The result is sexual incompatibility, producing either constant marital dissatisfaction or ultimate philandering leading to divorce.

Since it is not possible for every man to acquire either a broad, or indeed any, pre-marital experience, what is the solution? How can a wedded couple, or those about to wed, acquire at least a practical and sound approach to this problem without pre-marital experiment, which was a method advocated some twenty-five years ago and which, deservingly, caused widespread controversy. The following pages aim to satisfy that need.

Sexual normalcy has very definite bounds. A sexually normal woman, regardless of the depth of her passion, which can be considerable, has the capacity to be completely satisfied during a single relationship. She neither requires nor has the urge for repeated intimacies following the period of abatement; she does not crave them more frequently than at normal intervals, and she does not require an undue length of time for gratification. There are, indeed, abnormal women who enjoy and occasionally desire relationship three, four, and five times a day. They are prepared and willing at almost any time and can experience violent orgasms in every intimacy. We are not, of course, referring to prostitutes, who do not achieve orgasm with every man with whom they indulge, although there are nymphomaniacs who have taken up the occupation, not for financial gain, because some have come from wealthy families, but solely for the need of sexual gratification.

There is also the other type of oversexed woman, otherwise respectable, who, although having the capacity for satisfaction, nevertheless experiences at intervals such un-controllable desire that she will solicit the first man she meets. This, of course, no normal woman, even one capable of the most extreme abandon during sex relationships, could ever bring herself to do or ever has the impulse to do.

The only purpose in touching upon the matter of over-sexedness is to reassure many normal women who, in their relationships with their husbands, may hold themselves in check because they feel that complete abandonment to their impulses is a sign of depravity. It is intended to convince these women that their desires are perfectly normal as long as they are confined to any method of sexual gratification covered in these chapters. It is emphasized for such women that, unless they are victims of the abnormalities described, including frigidity—a complete lack of desire for sexual intimacy with any man—then they are perfectly normal regardless of the expression their passions may take.

Naturally, this does not include the perversions of sadism or masochism. Sadism is that form of sexual perversion in which the victim obtains gratification by imposing pain upon the partner by whipping or spanking, for example, while masochism is the direct opposite and involves gratification by subjection to the pain of whipping or spanking, to use the same illustration. There is no point in developing this phase further. It is psychopathic, thoroughly abnormal, and belongs only in a work devoted to the sick.

A final word of clarification on what has been said earlier in this section may be necessary, lest it be misconstrued. The impression may have been received that the desire or capacity for repeated intercourse is invariably an abnormality. This is not true. During the honeymoon period, repeated sex relations are the rule rather than the exception. The couple may enjoy themselves before going to sleep, before arising, and even once or twice during the day. This may go on steadily or diminishingly during their two weeks of happy relaxation or even longer, depending upon the length of the honeymoon and the healing of the bride's tenderness in the vaginal region.

However, this excess, and excess it is, would automatically and eventually abate of its own accord, but circumstances conspire to hasten the decline. Following the "glittering weeks," as the Germans call the honeymoon, the husband's business obligations interfere. He is away during the day, which eliminates any siesta intimacy, and is much to groggy and rushed in the morning to concentrate upon anything but reaching the office by nine o'clock. Outside of Saturday, Sunday, and holidays, he has only the evening, which for a time he may utilize as formerly. But even these occasions reduce themselves to three, two, and even one or less a week. That is the sex graph of our married lives.

Then there are other irregular intervals when, due to various factors, a man or woman may have the desire for repeated intercourse. However, these instances occur so infrequently as to involve not the slightest suggestion of abnormalcy. Even in these cases, a minimum fifteen-minute interval is required while the couple regenerate desire; this is mentioned because it frequently happens that a woman, immediately upon the completion of an intercourse abatement period of a minute or so which characterizes male reaction to the orgasm, will say, "I want you more than ever, now."

This is, by no means, to be construed as the wish of the

female for a repeated intercourse, even though immediate continuation would be such for the male. This desire on the woman's part results entirely from the fact that she was not completely satisfied and requires still further gratification. For her, it is not a repeated intercourse, but simply a continuation of the original one during which her husband disappointed her. Based solely, then, upon the limitations contained is this chapter, an individual can see that normal sexual behavior enjoys wide latitude, and that abnormality in this respect touches but few.

3.

The Erogenous Zones

WHILE the discussion up to this point has been general, it now becomes specific; what are the degrees of female passion, how does that passion express itself, how is it best aroused? All normal women will find themselves described in composite somewhere in this chapter.

To begin with, let us consider all the principal "spots of eroticism," that is, areas on the female body which have the capacity to stimulate desire when touched by the male lips, hands, or genitals. It might be stated first that the entire female body is an area of sexual excitation when caressed carefully by sensitive male hands. Just the feeling of their lovers' hands moving softly, gently, and tenderly anywhere about them will create a sensation of comfort and enjoyment in most women. This feeling, however, is a general one which will improve as attention becomes concentrated upon specific areas which have the power to produce definite thrills of excitement. For example, the ears, the cheeks, the mouth, neck, shoulders, bust, waist, stomach, hips, thighs, genitals, legs, when caressed by the male hands, will all react pleasantly to such a touch. But the hands are as nothing compared with the effectiveness of the mouth, lips, and tongue passing over the same areas.

The ear always is sensitive and responsive. The tongue chasing about the rim of it or moving within; the lips nuzzling all of it; or the teeth, lips, and tongue playing with the lobe of it, have the power to make some women pant, their breath hissing in and out at an unbelievable rate. These women who readily respond to toying with their ears are among the most easily aroused. Rapid panting likewise is the unfailing sign of a speedily aroused and highly passionate woman, a woman who requires a lengthy period for satisfaction.

Other women, however, can only momentarily withstand any playing with their ears. While the ensuing sensation is arousing, it is so only in a limited degree, and the result is a sensation more descriptive of the type that produces goose pimples. It has the effect, however, of making them wish to engage quickly in a passionate kiss; usually, immediately upon withdrawing their ear, they will turn their mouth actively upon their partner's. As might be assumed, this type of woman is slower to arouse, though not necessarily less passionate than the other, and will never express her emotion in the rapid panting above described.

But the ear is not always immediately responsive where the latter type of woman is involved. It might take a minute, at times, before the precise spot, or the precise manner of toying with it to produce reaction, is discovered. In this case, extending the heat of the breath to the area by a deep, slow exhalation will enhance its sensitivity. Notwithstanding, there are occasions also when it fails completely to react.

This has been emphasized because most men expect an immediate response from anything they may do. If, for example, they start toying with the female ear and their partner manifests no reaction, they immediately assume a lack of sensitivity there, and proceed elsewhere. This is unfortunate, because proper playing with a woman's ear or the adjoining area is one of the various factors of foreplay that contribute to arousing her, and it should not be neglected.

Another section of the female body as responsive as the ear in adding fuel to a woman's emotions is the area about the neck. The neck is most sensitive on the line running directly from the end of the shoulder to the ear, and to a point midway to the throat and midway to the direct center of the back of the neck. In other words, the throat and the section immediately adjoining it, and the area along the back of the neck, are not so sensitive as the area beneath the ear and the hollows found there. A woman will respond to kissing or light movements by the tongue on these sections precisely as she will to the ear, and the technique used to develop the sensitivity is the same.

The top surface of the shoulder also contains spots of eroticism that must be determined by experimentation, since the entire shoulder is not naturally an area of sensitivity. However, it definitely does contain areas every bit as sensitive as the neck.

We all know, of course, that the lips and the mouth, in addition to the clitoris and the vulva, always have the capacity to arouse passion, even assuming all other areas to be insensitive. Consequently, the kiss is the most important factor in foreplay, and he who does not constantly engage in it when his mouth is not otherwise occupied is a sorry lover, indeed. This holds true for every moment of foreplay as well as for the intercourse itself when performed in a position which allows it.

There are various types of kisses, and the standard Hollywood picture of half-parted lips, though it photographs well, may not necessarily be the kind appealing most to a woman. Some women, for example, prefer to kiss and be kissed with the insides of the lips. It is a warm, moist, intimate, and exciting exchange. Other women do little kissing themselves and prefer to be kissed, merely cutting off the air with their lips to allow proper suction. Still others may enjoy being kissed on the lower lip; that is, the lower lip is taken between both lips of her partner and sucked and worried by the tongue. For variety, the male may change to the upper lip, but such kisses involve only one of the female lips at a time. Again, there are those women who enjoy a kiss in which the male mouth envelops both of the female lips, sucking and teasing them lightly with the tongue. Then, too, there are others who prefer always the conventional type: to kiss and be kissed only with the outside of the lips pressed together. Of course, there is nothing too intimate about this type. Except for the fact that such a kiss is sustained longer by lovers, it is the kind normally exchanged between relatives.

The most intimate form of all, popular with at least fifty per cent of all woman and eighty per cent of the highly passionate, is the "French kiss'" or "soul kiss," as it is most generally called in this country. In this style, both lovers kiss open-mouthed, the female darting her tongue in and out of her partner's mouth while he does the same; both create a continuous movement with their tongues, and the male probably eventually draws his partner's tongue into his own mouth and holds it there.

Unhappily, nothing sounds less inviting than the kiss generally, and the "soul kiss" particularly, when brutally described in words. Since the latter is standard procedure for at least half the couples in this country and for the majority of Europeans, it must certainly have more to recommend it than verbal description. There are women who do not find too much enjoyment in the "soul kiss," and others who part their lips the moment a man leans forward to make love to them. Proper procedure requires that each woman be met in the manner that appeals to her the most, since successful sex practice is largely a matter of variety.

In addition to the kiss itself is the fervor with which it, as well as love-making in general, is administered. However, it can be stated positively that the great majority of women prefer their lover to be soft and gentle, for the kiss to be tender. There are, nevertheless, those who wish it to be fierce, almost painful. They prefer a rough, nearly bruising pressure by the male mouth upon their lips; when held, they wish to be squeezed to a point of breathlessness. Strangely, with regard to this matter of embrace, many women, even more or less moderate in their passion, have this desire, while preferring their kisses soft and tender. The majority of women, however, prefer gentleness throughout and it is largely the woman most expressive in her passion who either prefers or easily tolerates a roughness on the part of her lover.

The suitable technique for kissing and embracing is something the male must discover for himself by experiment with the individual woman to determine her preference, since it will not necessarily follow that every highly passionate woman, for example, desires roughness on the part of her lover. The best procedure to adopt is to assume initially that all women prefer gentleness and tendernesss, and determine their precise desires subsequently. While some females will definitely find roughness distasteful, none will object to a gentle approach, even though they may prefer a harsher treatment.

Next, and existing as one of the most prominent of the erogenous areas, are the female breasts. The sensitivity of the nipples alone is sufficient to reduce many girls and women to a state of helpless desire. Breast size has no bearing upon responsiveness. A flat-chested woman may react more intensely than her full-bosomed sister. The breasts, however, vary greatly in sensitivity as an agency of excitation, not only with respect to individual women but on occasion with an individual woman. Some women who experience a genital thrill as soon as the nipple is taken in the mouth will at other times experience practically no sensation other than warmth. The size of the nipple is no indication of sensitivity.

Under any circumstances, the fondling of the breasts or the massaging of the nipples is pleasant and comfortable for every woman. Considered from their average condition of responsiveness, it can be said that breast sensitivity ranges from one producing warmth without passion to one where arousal is almost immediate and desire for intercourse at once induced.

Although the breasts are responsive to hand fondling, the excitement that arises when they are kissed and suckled is normally a hundredfold more intense. Such emotion may register itself in a deep, shuddering sigh, in a light or heavy gasping, or in rapid panting; all are attended by closed eyes and an attitude leaving no doubt that the woman so excited has been gripped by a powerful seizure of sexual thrills. Many women react with a violent quivering which so shakes them from head to foot that the vibrations are easily felt; frequently, when a woman is very much in a sexual mood, this quivering is produced by kissing alone.

Women who react sharply to breast fondling are definitely in the minority and represent for the most part the highly passionate; another large group reacts exclusively with closed eyes and a deep, slow breathing. Sensation of enjoyment is immeasurably greater in the former, however, and of a quality which may be called intense even in the latter. In either case, both types of women are quickly aroused, although it does not necessarily follow that the latter will be equally expressive in intercourse. In fact, many women who will gasp when the nipple of the breast is taken in the mouth are definitely impassive in intercourse and may be only normally responsive in the genital area.

The majority of women, however, experience only a mild excitement from the handling or kissing of their breasts. Occasionally, the feeling extends itself to the genitals, depending upon the mood of the woman, but more frequently not. At any rate, with respect to such women, the breasts alone could never create an overpowering emotion or even a deep excitement, and are at best merely a contributing factor to the general creation of passion, as are the mouth and ear. Most of the women of this group are also of the individual orgasm type, a detailed discussion of which appears later, and generally are capable of only one or two orgasms unless their capacities are developed. On the other hand, at least one-quarter of this group possess an ability for numerous orgasms and a capacity for clitoral stimulation which is quite beyond that suggested by the weak responsiveness of their breasts.

The next erogenous zone as we move downward is the waist, sexually sensitive primarily to contact by the mouth and largely on the area directly above the hips and extending half way to the middle of the stomach. Mouth contact here, such as kissing or brushing with the tongue, produces a definite exciting effect directly upon the genital area, to which all women are subject in approximately the same degree.

The groins follow and, being directly adjacent to the

genitals, are sensitive to the touch of both hand and mouth. Strangely, in spite of the proximity of the groins to the genitals, the excitement that is induced by contact with that area is not even as great as that induced by caressing the breasts of women who are highly sensitive in that region. On the other hand, with respect to women who are not unduly sensitive in the breasts, the groin area has the invariable capacity to stimulate them.

We will ignore for a moment the interior and exterior genitals, because such areas are the most important of all, and much is to be said concerning them. Outside of these, only the insides of the thighs and the area directly above the knees remain to be considered. The inside sections of the thighs are particularly responsive to hand caressing and, when run over rapidly by the tongue, from knee to groin, can invoke a high pitch of excitement in both male and female. With respect to that area directly above the knee, it is strange but true that many normal women experience their highest degree of excitation when this area is continuously squeezed by the hand. It holds more of a thrill for them than mouth, breast, or ear kissing combined, and is sufficient in itself to produce the desire for intercourse. One might imagine that a woman possessing this peculiarity would be a highly emotional type, but she is among the most passive during the sex act.

It is interesting to observe that the buttocks, as well as the leg below the knee, are completely useless areas as excitants, so far as bedroom intimacy is concerned. Of course, these areas in contact when opposite sexes are clothed will naturally create desire, as when the calves of the leg or the knees are surreptitiously brought together under a table or in other close proximity. This is merely a matter of body contact, any form of which has the power to arouse two people who would like to be intimate but are unable to do so. However, this resolves itself very quickly into mere nothingness as soon as the couple are able to adopt the more intimate contact which bed and nudity allow.

These areas, then, with the exception of the genitals, comprise all the erogenous zones concentration upon which by the male can develop desire in the female. They are specific regions and every normal woman must be affected emotionally by some of them to a large degree if her partner understands his role. Before proceeding to the genitals, it may be well to recapitulate and reconsider the situation.

We see that the sexual nature of woman is a varying arrangement of emotional factors and that different women represent different combinations which may make one highly passionate, another moderately passionate, or place another on a still lower scale. It becomes apparent, too, that the precise combination making up a woman must be thoroughly understood by a man before he can treat her in a manner best suited to arouse and satisfy her to the fullest extent. It is clear, also, that the precise combination can never be determined beforehand, but that if a man is familiar with all the emotional factors which exist with respect to all women, he can recognize those which are absent or present in any specific woman and be able at least to evaluate her emotional make-up. It should be clear, too, that it will require more than one intimacy with a woman before all the factors in her nature can be determined, since on the first intercourse the male, as a rule, is unusually aroused and not able to delay orgasm sufficiently long to study her thoroughly. It is also clear that, unless a man has had these differences thoroughly explained to him or has had a personal experience broad enough to enable him to discover them for himself, he is bound to make mistakes either of omission or commission. Finally, it is obvious that no man with three or four isolated pre-marital affairs, or even a single extended one, is in a position to acquire more than a bare fundamental knowledge of the complicated and varying sexual nature that is a woman's. Neither can these be determined by questioning a woman. Since she does not know what is ordinary or unusual about herself, she does not know what pertinent information to volunteer.

We see, then, just to set down a few combinations, that some women are excited by soul kissing, that others are not; that the breasts of some females are highly responsive, that others are not; that some women with sensitive breasts are passive during intercourse; and that others with the same breast condition are intensely moved. These are just a few of the possibilities, but the women involved, although differently constructed, are in every case perfectly normal.

We reach now the vulva or external genitals. Eliminating those which have no bearing on sexual excitation, at least so far as male contact is concerned, there remain the clitoris, the small lips, the area surrounding the lips, and the vaginal entrance. Of all these, and by far the most important region and organ of the entire female body for inducing passion and effecting sexual gratification, is the clitoris. It is the most important because, when every other area of the body is insensitive to stimulation, the clitoris will not only induce excitement but will also bring about orgasm in the female. No man is or can be a qualified lover who is not thoroughy familiar with the power and peculiarities of this tiny but powerful organ.

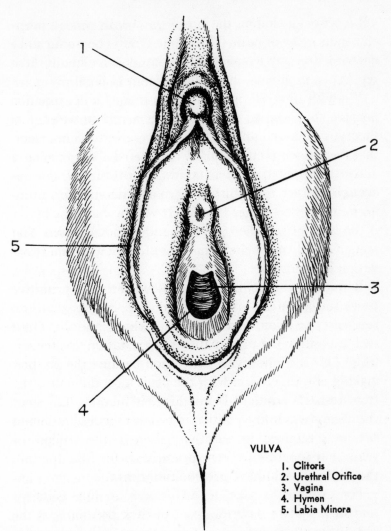

VULVA

1. Clitoris
2. Urethral Orifice
3. Vagina
4. Hymen
5. Labia Minora

There exists in this matter of the clitoris a strong difference of opinion among medical men themselves. Some regard it as does the writer, as the organ and area most conducive to sexual excitation and orgasm, while others contend that the vaginal entrance and adjacent area and vagi-

nal interior, including the tip of the womb, should properly induce the orgasm. This latter group goes so far as to contend that any woman who is not sensitive about these regions is impotent—incapable of normal orgasm.

We wish to dwell upon this for a moment, because it is possible that women may encounter a text in which this theory is discussed and, as a result, receive the impression that there is something sexually disordered about them and allow it to prey upon their minds. Unfortunately, there is enough of fact to disturb a woman without adding unnecessary fiction to her burden. It will probably be better if the basis of this theory is expounded for all to see. The reader can then conclude for himself on how firm a foundation it stands.

Regarding this opinion, it is contended that in primitive times sexual intercourse was conducted largely from the rear entry position, that is, animal fashion, and that from such a position the principal seat of excitation was the clitoris. This is a mystifying conclusion because the position making clitoral contact with the penis most difficult is the front-to-back position. If anything, it follows that, since the clitoris was in the position to be most ignored, it should not have retained its sensitivity through the millions of years that separate us from primitive man. Like the tail, the clitoris should have become rudimentary.

For argument's sake, let us assume an impossibility: that in primitive days the front-to-back position was the conventional one and, as such, was the one allowing greatest clitoral contact with the penis. Where does this theory venture from there? It continues itself in the elaboration that in the course of development to civilization the front-to-front position become the conventional one and that in this position the clitoris is scarcely touched by the organ.

Stopping here for a moment, it must be clear to everyone that the front-to-front position allows, if anything, the nearest possible clitoral contact, since in some cases an overdeveloped clitoris when erected can touch the male penis. The theory concludes by saying that to meet this change, woman is now presumed to be in a transitional stage in which the nerve centers are being transferred from the ignored clitoris to the vaginal area and that, "anthropologically speaking," it will take a few million years for this transfer to be completed. For the next two or three million years, then, all women who are not sensitive about the vagina must be considered impotent or abnormal!

The reader can draw his own conclusions with respect to the reasonableness of such an explanation. The writer regards it as a far-fetched basis on which to contend that a woman who is sensitive only to clitoral contact is impotent, not sexually normal.

However, this is not the only theory advanced to explain the lack of vaginal sensitivity in women responsive only to clitoral stimulation. Another, even more prevalent, accounts for it in an entirely different manner, but reaches the same conclusion, namely, that the women are not sexually normal. It is well to discuss this, also, and allow the female reader to form an opinion of the extent to which such a theory may be relied upon.

This belief holds that most women have practiced constant clitoral masturbation in their adolescence. As a result, attention has become focussed upon the clitoris so that in maturity they experience no sensation elsewhere. However, this view, even if the findings are trustworthy, is hardly convincing.

To begin with, masturbation is practiced far more extensively and with greater frequency by boys than by girls. Hardly a youth escapes it. By the same analogy, then, men should be far more responsive when orgasm is induced by the female hand than by the sex act; we all know that there is no truth to this.

Since those women who respond in greater measure to clitoral than to vaginal contact form the great majority, it is more reasonable to assume that the minority have highly developed nervous systems than that the majority should have underdeveloped systems. Also, the nature of orgasm is of a different character in these two types of women, as is thoroughly explained in a succeeding chapter. It generally follows, too, that when a woman is sensitive about the vagina, her breasts are proportionately sensitive, whereas the breasts of the others are usually unresponsive. Since no woman stimulates herself by fondling her mammae, all breasts should exhibit equal sensitivity, and we know that they definitely do not.

Therefore, it can be accepted without concern by any woman that it is a perfectly normal condition to be sensitive only in the clitoral zone and nowhere else, just as it is also normal, but less usual, to be highly sensitive throughout the entire vaginal area. When the reader also becomes acquainted with the other sexual differences among women which are to be described, he will clearly understand why a difference in sensitivity about the vulva is neither remarkable nor surprising, but should, if anything, be expected in the light of all other varying factors which constitute a woman's individual sexual make-up.

This belief in widespread adolescent female masturbation is subject to doubt. Its reliability depends entirely upon the character of the survey. Figures gathered from hospital records will very probably reveal a high percentage of those addicted to the practice, particularly if the patients are suffering from some form of sexual or nervous disorder. By the same token, a similar investigation based on the habits of college girls should also show a high percentage, because the average female student is more likely to be high-strung than the working daughter of a day laborer. Furthermore, such a breakdown should also take into consideration whether the girl attends a coeducational institution or an all-girl school. A coeducational college should show a lower proportion than the other, because there the girls have a greater opportunity to relieve excess sexual energy. However, since college women form only a fraction of our female population, any figures applying to them exclusively or in large proportion, would hardly justify the conclusion that the majority of women have practiced adolescent masturbation.

In any case, however, the most important figure to be determined in connection with this subject is the age at which masturbation was first indulged in, if we are to make any comparison between male and female incidence. If the average woman started at the age of sixteen, seventeen, or thereafter, this bears no relationship to masturbation as practiced by men, who commence the habit much earlier, at twelve, thirteen, or fourteen—long before they are having any steady association with girls. In other words, boys begin to enter into this form of sex outlet at an age when their adolescence cannot possibly be in question, while girls of sixteen, seventeen, eighteen, or older have a much higher degree of sexual maturity, are nearer the adult stage, and for that matter can be already regarded as sexual adults. Therefore, when one speaks of adolescent female masturbation, the expression should be qualified to avoid forming a picture of twelve, thirteen, and fourteen-year-old girls who engage with themselves with practically the same frequency and in the same proportion as boys.

Since it is generally agreed that an area of high sensitivity exists within the clitoris, let us consider its function in sexual activity. The clitoris is a small neck-like organ, varying in length, but on the average three-quarters of an inch to an inch long. Most of it is buried beneath the surface, leaving only the glans or tip, a knob-like section generally about an eighth of an inch wide, exposed. It is located approximately where the small lips, traveling in the upward direction, merge. When a woman is not aroused, this little organ is limp and insensitive; the tip inclined to recede beneath the skin; unless one knows exactly where it lies, the finger running over the area could very easily overlook it. A surpisingly large number of men and women are completely unaware of its existence, and it is doubtful if many who have heard of it know precisely where to locate it.

As soon as a woman becomes excited, the clitoris erects itself and loses its soft pliability very much as does the male penis under excitation. The tip, then, can be distinctly felt and almost the entire organ can be traced along the surface. Contact can build up in it the most delightful feeling, finally culminating in the most exquisite of all sensations, the orgasm. While the tip of the clitoris usually extends only slightly above the surface, many such organs encountered protrude considerably farther; still others barely protrude at all, and the tip can be detected only by pressure upon the spot. If a husband has difficulty in locating this knob-like organ, it is advisable that his wife undergo an immediate examination. It is possible that adhesions are preventing erection and the emergence of the glans. In fact, this should be one of the precise factors determined in the pre-marital physical examination suggested in the opening chapter.

However, even under normal conditions, it is not difficult to understand why so many men and women are unaware of the existence of this vital organ. Since most men are inclined to approach the genital region of a woman before she is sufficiently aroused by foreplay, the clitoris is not in the erected state, and it feels little different from any of the other tissue about the vaginal area. Also, since its location is considerably above the vagina, it passes unnoticed even when erected, because most men concentrate their attention about or within the vaginal entrance. Furthermore, in spite of its sensitivity, the clitoris frequently requires minutes of gentle massaging not only to bring it to erection but even to develop sensation.

As a result, it is not unnatural that even men who are aware of the precise location and of the abilities of the clitoris, having attempted to stimulate it and not meeting with immediate response, assume that the woman in question is not sensitive there and have permanently abandoned it as an erogenous region. Nor does higher education on the part of an individual necessarily indicate knowledge in this connection. There exist college graduates of both sexes who, far from knowing its peculiarities, have never even heard of the clitoris.

While this organ is the throne upon which orgasm sits for all females, sensation for at least forty per cent of women, if not more, is located *exclusively* there. These women, we shall refer to in the future as the "lowly sensitive." Regarding this group, the other areas of the vulva, as well as the vaginal interior, are *completely* insensitive, and where any sensation at all exists there, it is so slight as to be of no consequence. Most unhappily, nature has committed an oversight here, as she occasionally does, and it is this, in addition to the difficulty most men have in delaying orgasm, that contributes almost wholly to sexual incompatibility or lack of sexual satisfaction on the part of the female.

Another third, approximately, to whom we shall refer as the "moderately sensitive," have only a moderate sensitivity about the vulva, exclusive of the clitoris. While this group is capable of orgasm independent of clitoral contact with the finger or penis, it relies largely upon a rapid, violent rhythm which sets up a disturbance in the entire genital area. This violent motion, characterized by deep penetrations into the vagina, also has the power by the force of its drive to bring the area above the penis itself into contact with the clitoris and to create a strong aggravation about the external parts above the vagina which may extend even to the clitoral zone.

Such a woman also characteristically engages in fierce genital wriggling, even meeting the male in his drive, as if to force the clitoris, and perhaps so doing on occasion, against the male organ and causing the penis to bend. If the male orgasm can be delayed, or rather delays itself long enough—this violent type of male makes no effort himself to exercise control, and movement of this kind will not allow a retarded male orgasm—the woman may have her climax, and it will usually occur simultaneously with that of the male. She may miss it, however, if she is slow to respond or if, following his orgasm, the male does not continue the rhythm long enough for her to reach her climax.

Females of this physical temperament usually desire a violent male—a sort of sexual battering ram—and are the strongest in their preferences, evidently having discovered that a penis of average size or less, and a man more reserved in his habits, fails to satisfy her if he allows the clitoris to take care of itself, which most men do. She is, however, a type definitely capable of more than one orgasm if properly handled, but she will frequently be denied them with the kind of man she seeks; this violent type of male concentrates too fully upon his own pleasure to give any deep study to hers. Nevertheless, because they feel the need for such a sexual partner, women of this nature are mentally conditioned to stimulation by a broad chest, knotted arms, and bulging legs. They believe that a man so built is a type of masculinity capable of being a violent lover. He is all of that but, as the partner of many women, he would create a dislike for the sex act.

A great number of women, although definitely the minority, are more fortunate. These will be referred to as the "highly sensitive." Their entire genital surface is a mass of sexual sensitivity, as is the vaginal cavity itself. Quite obviously, these women have nervous systems which are more highly developed sexually than those of the majority, because the nerve mechanism which exists in the clitoral zone does not extend throughout the entire genital area of a woman—as least, not visibly. One may assume that the area operates sympathetically and that it is a matter of nerve development.

At any rate, this minority, in addition to being sensitive at the clitoris, is also highly sensitive about the small lips, the adjacent area, the entrance to the vagina, and the area deep within the vaginal canal at the point where the neck of the womb protrudes; this is known as the "vaginal vault." In fact, wherever contact by either the hand or penis is made anywhere within this area, sensation starts to flow and orgasm can be reached and sustained without any friction with the clitoris whatever.

One might imagine that a woman so sensuously constructed could hardly fail to achieve sexual satisfaction and that to do so would be a relatively simple matter. However, such a woman is not without her problems. Her orgasms may be lengthy and require a longer sustaining period for gratification; should she be married to a man who exercises no orgastic restraint whatever, she suffers intensely. Conversely, her husband, a man of the best intentions, may not be able to delay his orgasm sufficiently long. She may have desires she is inhibiting, such as oral contact with the genitals, which will be discussed in another section, and is fearful of shocking her husband. As a rule, this highly sensitive type leans strongly and practically without exception to oral rhythm. So, regardless of temperament, sexual incompatibility may always exist in some way or another.

These, then, are all the normal erogenous zones and their varying degrees of sensitivity. We are not discussing purely individual zones, peculiar to some women, which have developed as the result of some psychological factor; only those common to all. It is necessary now to discuss the sexual temperament of women with respect to these areas in responding to foreplay.

4.

The Technique of Foreplay

THE fact that most women are sensitive in the genital region largely at the clitoris does not mean at all that they will react even approximately in the same manner to orgasm or to the emotions leading up to it. They have the same organs, it is true, but not necessarily the same nerve structure or similar temperament apart from their sexual natures. Some women are naturally more reserved than others, some less inhibited, some more imaginative, some more broad-minded, some more modest, to note only a few distinctions. Quite obviously, they can vary in numerous other ways. Undoubtedly some of these variations, while not necessarily interfering with ultimate sexual gratification, though some do, interpose obstacles to it. The reason for a quirk in the nature of an individual can lie either in her background, in her inheritance, or in her endowment.

For instance, a girl reared under the influence of a mother whose habit it is to talk contemptuously of sex, due probably to her own unsatisfactory sex life, may develop an aloofness toward it in the daughter. The daughter, though susceptible to sexual excitation, may be in constant conflict with her mental conception, making her difficult, but not impossible, to arouse. Mental attitude is the most important factor in successful sexual intimacy.

It may also occur that a girl is brought up in a home environment where demonstrativeness and outward expression of affection are subdued. Such a girl, married to a man from a similar environment, can hardly be expected to react to foreplay as would a woman coming from a household where outward manifestations of affection are lavish and constant.

On the other hand, there are many girls, maturing in a reserved atmosphere, who respond greedily to affection, although their sisters may take after the parents. In this respect, nature has constructed a highly passionate girl by birth, and no amount of parental coldness can stifle her desires. If anything, she is starved for affection. Of course, her partner's nature must be reciprocal if it is to encourage hers.

Then, there are women whose attitude toward sex and to the male and his sexual habits is one of modified revulsion at the outset, but capable of subsequent change. In these cases, it frequently happens that, as children, their bedrooms adjoined that of their parents, and they have heard their fathers attempting to force their mothers into intimacy on occasions when the women had no desire for it. One does not know, of course, whether the husbands were unreasonable in their demands. The normal man rarely is unreasonable as to frequency, and it can be suspected that the mothers had their share of responsibility in the matter.

Regardless of where the fault lies, the children become victims; it might be remarked that cases of this kind are not uncommon. To induce in such girls a normal attitude toward men and sex is entirely a matter of approach, and the male who would break down this reserve must proceed with caution and never attempt to use force or haste.

There is no need to examine all of the factors which may affect sexual temperament. They are too numerous, and they serve simply to illustrate what can happen to increase the tendency of most women to be slow to arouse. In the majority of the cases, however, it will not be known just what causes a woman to be slow in response; a husband will know only that she is slow or difficult. Consequently, she must be handled in a manner which always takes all possible factors into consideration. Once a man fully realizes that the sexual disposition of a woman parallels his in only the most minor degree, there will be less sexual incompatibility.

It is well to explain at this point what is meant by foreplay and the proper but neglected procedure concerning it. Foreplay consists of the love-making, however a couple engages in it, which stimulates passion and precedes actual intercourse. Properly practiced, it should comprise two parts: during the first half, all contact with the female genital region by either the hand or the male organ should be kept at an absolute minimum. A man has every portion of the female body except that area upon which to concentrate, and an adequate lover can thus induce excitement sufficient in most cases even for intercourse.

The second half of foreplay should concentrate upon the female genital area even if the male be simultaneously kissing his partner's mouth or her breasts. Foreplay should never last less than fifteen minutes even though a woman may be sufficiently aroused in five. The other ten minutes properly utilized can stimulate her to even greater heights of excitement. The only exception to this should occur when a woman requests intercourse sooner or if she has attained her maximum pitch of excitement and is beginning to cool. This can easily happen in the case of a woman of average passion who is not completely in the mood.

Foreplay should never run less than fifteen minutes because this is not too generous a period in which to extend a woman's pleasure. Some wives are just beginning to experience a clitoral erection at the end of that time; others require an even longer period. Numerous women begin to experience a clitoral sensation only at the end of a half hour. Proper handling, of course, can reduce this period considerably, but it requires patience and understanding.

Although there is a minimum period for foreplay, there is no maximum, beyond the two exceptions mentioned. Just as cooling can be detected, there is also a definite guide by which to judge the extent of a woman's excitement and her readiness for intercourse. This will be treated shortly, and is one of the most important pieces of knowledge that a husband can possess with respect to his wife. With it, he can be absolutely certain that he will not engage in intercourse before his partner is ready, something the average man too frequently is careless about.

So far, then, we have considered the normal erogenous zones; their varying sensitivity, both generally and with respect to individual women; the fact that different combinations of sensitive areas will vary sexual responsiveness in women; and the fact that a woman's nature may either assist or interfere with the operation of normal sexual machinery. It is now necessary to know how these factors further affect the sexual process.

With respect to foreplay, most women—the lowly and moderately sensitive, together forming the majority—are more or less silent and passive aside from the usual squirming that is customary as male and female bodies press closely together. All women, however, even the highly sensitive, are disposed to allow the male to arouse them; they do not give too much thought to his particular emotion, seeming to assume it will take care of itself, which it generally does.

The extent of female passion, regardless of its degree, forces the woman to concentrate largely upon herself; this is especially true of the highly passionate types, who will not hesitate to express their desires if they are completely uninhibited. Such activity as any woman engages in is either involuntary or tends to increase her own emotion. If by chance such behavior also excites the male, it is purely coincidental unless it be deliberately done for the purpose of arousing an unenthusiastic or slow partner.

Although the highly sensitive type of woman may be inactive during foreplay but intensely emotional during intercourse, she is more inclined to activity, as would be expected, and is also the most quickly aroused. She can reach a point of excitement in the first half of foreplay which the majority of women attain only after full foreplay, and is ready for the sex act at almost any time. She may wrestle until subdued, thereafter remaining perfectly quiet; she may roll, rise to her knees, and then throw herself on her back or stomach, repeating the routine until locked into immobility by the male. She may have an uncontrollable impulse to bite even before intercourse, and will do serious damage to her partner's lips unless he guards himself. More rarely, she will exhibit the tendency to kiss violently, practically smothering the male's mouth and at the same time forcing her breasts and body into the closest proximity with his. She may be seized with uncontrollable body jerks as soon as the male places an arm about her, and such spasms may continue for several minutes. All these various manifestations of emotions are usually accompanied by heavy breathing or panting and occasional deep, drawn-out sighs.

As the first half of foreplay continues and passion mounts, many women will repeatedly employ terms of violent affection. In other words, many women want to express themselves in terms of endearment, while others wish to hear such expressions. Some women, even those of respectable background, will employ incredible smut, repeating sidewalk words as added thrills overtake them; others talk a fantastic nonsense, disconnected and childish. No woman, however, wishes to speak during orgasm.

All of these various emotional make-ups are perfectly normal, the women in no degree being oversexed. They merely possess a sense of passion more acute than that of the majority and deep enough to drive inhibitions from their minds. All react during foreplay in a manner similar to that which has been described, and occasionally even in the first half of it.

It is also well to indicate, since we are discussing the highly passionate group, which is also the highly sensitive group, just what manner of foreplay arouses them. As a consequence of the various factors, such as the degree of sensitivity in the erogenous zones or the individual natures which make up a woman's sexual temperament, it should be clear that all women will not respond in the same manner to identical stimuli. Some women who react intensely to the effect of kissing can be aroused quickly, perhaps in two minutes, by simply being pressed close to their partner, their lips engaged in whatever type of kiss most appeals to them. Others may require this and the added stimulus of some slight or strong genital squirming as externals are pressed against externals or as the female genitals are rubbed against the male thigh. There are others who, after a minute of such intimacy, will ask for the immediate insertion of the penis, desiring even that foreplay take place from the most intimate position. Still others enjoy, even more than the mouth kiss, the kissing and fondling of their breasts, becoming so aroused and enraptured as to be ready immediately thereafter for intercourse. Others may enjoy a combination of mouth, neck, and breast kissing while the male hands explore the waist, hips, and the outside and inside of the thighs, or squeeze gently the area just above the knees. Still others enjoy the proximity of the penis between their breasts. Ninety per cent of the highly passionate group have an overwhelming desire to caress the male organ orally, approaching it with a suddenness and directness which leaves no doubt that the impulse and desire are overpowering. Others enjoy being kissed by sections, their partners starting at the mouth and covering all the erogenous zones in order as the women lie their in a gasping ecstasy. Throughout the time these various procedures are taking place, the highly sensitive type of woman is experiencing in her genital region definite sensations which occur in the lowly and moderately sensitive usually only when the genitals are directly stimulated.

The highly passionate types, the most expressive in their passion, require no genital stimuli to prepare them for the sex act; however, no man should neglect this phase because, unlike the majority of women, a good measure of the male's excitement is inspired by handling the genital area of the female.

Perhaps the reader will now understand what was meant when it was stated previously that what may seem unusual to the inexperienced may be quite ordinary to the initiated. One who constantly and successfully pursues women must so frequently encounter females of the type just described that their behavior seems as commonplace as that of the unresponsive woman who can attain only one orgasm. An inexperienced man who has had limited sexual association, or an uninformed woman of only moderate sensitivity, might easily regard the more highly passionate type as being abnormally sensitive when, in fact, they are no less normal than other women.

The moderately passionate mother who reads this may very well have a daughter who falls into the above group; her child's sexual make-up is something with which no mother can be completely familiar. Hence, it is *criminal negligence* for any parent to assume that a daughter can always be trusted to exercise self-control and can therefore be given unrestricted freedom with the opposite sex.

Although foreplay should be lengthy, it could, as has been said, be quite short with a highly sensitive woman, because the quality of her passion is much like a consuming fire which spreads rapidly. Nevertheless, if extended foreplay is employed, as it should be with every woman, it acts as fuel added to an already white-hot blaze.

Genital stimuli, when applied to this type and added to a pitch of excitement which is already fever high, will result in a condition of ecstasy that will bring about immediate orgasm if not carefully controlled by the male. Although many women request intercourse soon after their partner engages in sex play, controlled maintenance of the latter will produce in the female a rapture which can be continuous until the male is ready to engage in the intercourse.

Up to this point, then, the highly passionate woman, a member of the minority, has been discussed in detail as to her emotional make-up, desires, impulses, and response to foreplay. She will be shown to be a complex creature, less capable of being fitted into a routine pattern of treatment than the majority of women who will now be discussed. This is because her impulses and a more highly sex-sensitive nature may cause her to respond with unusual rapidity and fierceness on one occasion and smouldering lassitude on another. However, the unmistakable symptoms of volcanic heat are always to be recognized in her rapid panting and the unrealistic mood which seems to overcome her. It is apparent that she has entered a world of her own where there exists nothing but overwhelming passion. For this reason, although it is always well to start out systematically, it is best to accommodate her impulses and desires and follow wherever they lead, since she is demonstrative in her emotion and automatically selects a course best calculated to arouse her to the blazing emotion that is characteristic of her.

The majority of women, the moderately and lowly sensitive, likewise exhibit variations; some are more passionate than others. However, they all generally fall into an uncomplicated method of procedure in which time for adequate arousal is the important element. As has already been stated, such women are more or less passive and silent during foreplay, aside from the squirming which takes place in close embrace. They are content to allow the male to arouse them.

A single phase of foreplay is not sufficient to excite them to the emotional heights of which even in their limited way they are capable. One must utilize every technique to arouse them to a point equalling that attained by their more passionate sisters in only the first part of foreplay. Osculation, for example, while intensely enjoyed, will not produce the panting, deep sighs, or the violent quivering which a single kiss will induce in the highly passionate. The ear or neck, concentrated upon by the male, will add only a little fuel to the flame. The male hands, moving over the female body and avoiding the genital area, have the capacity to induce but a limited emotion, generally insufficient to cause an erection of the clitoris. And so it goes with any combination of hand or mouth procedures involved in the first part of foreplay. It is usually possible to excite such women only so far.

Nevertheless, this phase, though not necessarily invoking an intense degree of passion, is highly pleasurable to such a woman, and she has no objection to an indefinite continuance of it. It stimulates, of course, a desire for something more enveloping, but she is far from overwhelmed and submerged in the drive of her own emotion. It is only when, in the second part, the male hand begins to stroke and caress the external genitals that she begins to experience a definite, mounting increase of emotion, although this area generally, outside of the clitoris, can produce no orgastic sensation whatever in the lowly sensitive. It is as though this region were deadened by a local anesthetic.

This must be clearly understood by the male as well as by the woman herself. Although it has been said that stroking the vulva, with the exception of the clitoris, will produce little or no sensation of gathering orgasm, it does, nevertheless, increase passion. This reaction is mental rather than physical, because it registers on the female mind that her lover is now engaged with the most intimate part of her body, and this realization is exciting. Just as the mind of a man dwelling upon an intimate situation with a woman will produce desire and erection, although not orgasm or any of the physical sensation associated with orgasm, so the fact that her lover is now occupied with this private section of her body will likewise induce greater excitement on the part of the female.

As his hand, however, begins to stroke the clitoris, causing its erection or developing it, a definite physical sensation suggesting indescribable pleasure begins to take place, and it is at this point that the lowly and moderately sensitive may be said to start experiencing the drive with which the highly sensitive are imbued almost at the beginning.

It must be realized, of course, that there are also varying degrees of passion within the ranks of the lowly and moderately sensitive and that these two groups represent the majority of women. The only characteristic distinguishing them is the length of time required to produce an orgasm or the number of which they are capable. Let it be assumed, for example, that, following the first part of foreplay, a woman requires five minutes of clitorial excitation to create orgasm. Such a woman would, naturally, be more quickly aroused and consequently regarded as more sensitive than a woman who requires fifteen minutes, provided the orgastic period were the same for both. Also, a woman who, following clitoral excitation, experiences two orgasms would likewise be more sensitive or passionate than one who experiences less. However, in the preliminaries of foreplay, the responsiveness to sexual stimulation is generally the same. These women are impassive and inactive, and are not necessarily aroused to an emotional pitch by reason of presence in bed, nudity, or intimate proximity.

It might be well to mention also that all women, the highly sensitive as well as others, are at times more subject to sexual emotion than at others, frequently just prior to menstruation, during it, or immediately following. On these occasions, they are capable of quicker arousal, and the clitoris will be found in an approximate state of erection when the partner turns his attention to it. Orgasm can also be induced more rapidly and will be more intense. This condition can result also from a number of other factors, but these occasions are not too frequent and will scarcely involve more than two or three out of every ten relationships indulged in by the married woman.

There is still one other type of woman who is as distinctive in her way as is the highly passionate. This type is much like the majority in that she is not too expressive in her emotion during foreplay. That she does, however, clearly become absorbed in sexual excitement is indicated by her repeated opening or rolling her eyes upward and then closing them. Her most distinguishing feature, however, is the number of separate orgasms she has the capacity to experience consistently during every relationship; these vary in number from five to ten. She also resembles the majority in that her climaxes must be clitorally induced; contrariwise, she is unlike them in that she can be aroused, not so speedily as the highly sensitive, but more rapidly than the others. Her orgasm is of the same individual type as that of the majority of women. (There are two types of orgasms, both of which will be described and graphically illustrated in a subsequent chapter.) This latter type of woman is the most difficult of all to satisfy. Any interference with her mood or error in procedure can operate to reduce the number of orgasms she will experience on any given occasion. This places a certain amount of strain upon the husband who tries to make the most of a relationship for her.

We have now described all the various types of normal women who constitute partners in sexual intimacy. They have been discussed as to their ability to respond emotionally and physically, as to their tastes and desires, as to the manner of their emotional and physical expression, and as to their personal feelings as revealed through foreplay. Since the writer divides the performance of a sexual relationship into three parts, namely foreplay, intercourse, and abatement, it is now appropriate to discuss the second and most important phase, intercourse itself.

5.

The Nature of Intercourse

IN a previous chapter it was stated that there exists a
definite guide for determining the readiness of a woman
for intercourse. It is an unfailing signal. Unless it clearly
manifests itself, a woman has not been sufficiently aroused
and has not reached a high peak of her excitement prior to
the sex act. No intelligent or considerate lover should force
intercourse until this signal appears.

This guide is the amount of slippery secretion that issues
primarily from a region just below the vaginal entrance
and, secondarily, within the vagina. It is a viscous, pale,
transparent fluid, varying in texture. In some females, particularly in those who have not borne children and in
younger girls, it is thinner in quality; generally, however, it
is of about the same consistency. If a woman has been
thoroughly aroused, this emanation, provided by nature as
a necessary lubricant, can be distinctly felt upon stroking
the vulva, and it allows itself to be easily spread over the
entire area. It flows from Bartholin's glands, two small
glands, located within the small lips and slightly beneath
the vaginal entrance. The vaginal interior will be found
to contain a similar secretion seeping from the uterus into
the vaginal vault. This allows the canal walls to become
adequately coated and ease the friction caused by the in-
cessant motion of the male organ. The penis also emits a
like substance, so that lubrication does not depend ex-

clusively upon the female organs. Since Bartholin's glands are located in the lower part of the vulva, the fluid naturally pools there. It must be brought up by the male finger to coat the clitoris and surrounding area to avoid their chafing.

So long as a woman is excited, this fluid flows continuously and abundantly. Every woman knows how moist and uncomfortable she may feel at times following some minor intimacy. When she begins to cool, the flow ceases at once, the area dries with surprising rapidity, and continued friction upon it will result in painful irritation.

This fluid must not be confused with the general moistness that is constant about the interior and exterior genitals; no experienced man will so mistake it. These areas consist of mucous membrane which must remain moist if dryness and roughness are to be avoided. For that reason, the genital region will at all times feel moist upon contact, but the moistness is of a light, watery consistency which immediately dries with friction, whereas the other appears in far greater quantity, increasing in amount as excitement increases, is definitely slippery in body, and continues to flow so long as a woman requires satisfying, should it be fifteen minutes or an hour. Unless this fluid issues in unmistakable quantity, nature is indisputably indicating that a woman is not yet prepared for intercourse and must be further stimulated; as soon as she is ready, nature never fails to release the fluid in abundance.

There are occasional instances, however, when, in arranging for the proper satisfaction of a woman, nature will require assistance. A *considerate* wife is ready and willing at all times, barring certain days, to accommodate her husband's sexual needs, just as the considerate husband is alert to fulfill his wife's requirements. Such women and such men are usually happily married. This type of wife goes even further. Although she may not feel in the mood for one reason or another, her husband coming home from work may not be aware of this. Since she senses an amorous mood on his part, she either does not make her feelings known or deprecates them at bedtime. She may even initiate the preliminaries herself. The consequence is that, despite all the proper observance of foreplay, particularly with a woman of the lowly sensitive type, the husband will discover when his hand reaches the genital area that the fluid has not yet started to flow and try as he may, he cannot induce it to flow. He will also discover, as he continues to stroke the genitals, that he cannot produce a sensation in the clitoris, that the area becomes dry; and he will observe obvious twinges of very definite pain due to chafing if he persists.

Of course, the proper thing to do is to abandon intimacy for that night; if the wife is not aroused, as indicated by the failure of the fluid to flow, she will not be disturbed by a discontinued relationship. However, if he fails to desist, it is understandable; he is excited, and there is no doubt that his wife, who has already proved her thoughtfulness, will insist upon his satisfying himself.

The solution is very simple, and will result in complete satisfaction all around. A forefinger dipped in vaseline, cold cream, hand lotion, or similar convenient substance, and applied to the externals, will lubricate the area so that without pain to his wife he can devote himself to a stimulation of the clitoris, which in time will respond by developing sensation. However, no woman in a normal mood will ever require an artificial lubricant, and notwithstanding any advice to the contrary, an artificial lubricant should never be used as a constant or general practice. The natural flowing of the fluid is a man's best guide to the emotional pitch of his partner, and the indiscriminate use of artificial lubricants circumvents the very thing that nature has sought to provide: a foolproof signal as to the opportuneness of the intercourse. Furthermore, something is decidedly wrong either with a husband's technique or his wife's physical condition if artificial lubricants must constantly be resorted to.

It is now assumed that the woman is well lubricated and ready for the intercourse. How does she respond? Let us first consider the highly passionate type. It is in this phase of the relationship more than in any other that such a female distinguishes herself from the majority and makes it difficult for any man to delay his own orgasm; she may require five to thirty minutes or even more to satisfy herself, depending upon the extent of her passion. Since, as is explained in a chapter dealing with self-control on the part of the male, the masculine instinct is to achieve a speedy orgasm, it is obvious that his self-restraint will be abnormally taxed.

To begin with, a highly passionate woman requires no clitoral stimulation whatever during intercourse itself, since she is a mass of genital sensation internally and externally. Furthermore, her type of orgasm differs materially from that of others, which a subsequent diagram will illustrate clearly. She experiences what may be described as a sustained orgasm and almost from the moment the penis is inserted until the end of the period required for her satisfaction, she undergoes a continuous sensation of rapture which gradually bores into her nervous system and eventually results in satiety, swooning, sobbing, or the inability for further copulation. Any of these four reactions is immediately heightened by the male orgasm regardless of when it occurs, and a simultaneous climax need not be considered, since her entire sensation is practically one sustained orgasm. Furthermore, any highly sensitive woman can experience all four reactions over a period of time, not necessarily during one relationship, but a different one on different occasions; these represent merely the four levels of excitement. Although it is unusual for a girl or woman to experience more than one or two consistently, one can encounter women who travel the entire range.

Satiety usually requires the longest time to achieve; the woman involved seems better conditioned to withstand the height of sensation than do women of the other three levels. Hence, she can revel in her excitement until her appetite is thoroughly satisfied. She herself, rather than her nervous system, brings the relationship to an end.

Swooning comes next in time, because in this instance a woman withstands the sensation, craving more and more, until nature finally intrudes by throwing her into a faint.

Sobbing follows, but not far behind; the woman herself suddenly breaks off the relationship in a wild, uncontrollable burst of tears which shakes her completely. She requires several minutes of tender quieting.

Finally, and covering relatively the shortest period, is the simple inability further to withstand sensation. In this case, the woman is unable to allow it to carry her as far as the swooning or sobbing stage; after having asked her partner a number of times previously to desist for a moment, she finally directs him to stop altogether.

Those readers who have ever laughed themselves into a fit of crying will recognize that it is characteristic to laugh at a certain level for a time, the level rising until the limit of endurance is reached. Then, one finds the laughter automatically changing to tears and becoming disagreeable.

Furthermore, at no time during a sex relationship, when passion is at its peak or approaching it, will the countenances of either man or woman ever take on an appearance of pleasurable or peaceful relaxation. To the contrary, the features are distorted as if the partners were undergoing severe pain rather than experiencing the most exquisitely delightful of all sensations.

For the benefit of those women who form the majority and who may wonder how orgasm can drive a woman to tears, it should be stated it is common knowledge that tears can be produced by a reaction diametrically opposed to sorrow. The sensation of joy so frequently experienced when women and children, long separated, are reunited is also accompanied by tears. It is not to be wondered at, then, that those women who experience the pleasure of intense orgasm are also uncontrollably moved to violent weeping.

All of these four levels may vary in length of time with different women. The period may also vary for the same women, depending upon her mood. As a rule, however, it is usually of consistent duration, unless shortened by the inability of the male to delay his orgasm.

To a male unaccustomed to a violent climax, the situation is startling. One can understand that he is shocked when a woman suddenly emits a series of piercing screams loud enough to waken a neighborhood and to suggest that she is being abused. His heart practically stands still. He experiences somewhat the same reaction when a woman who is violently panting, gasping, scratching, and biting suddenly heaves a tremendous sigh and becomes limp and insensible, or seemingly so. Her partner's first thought is that she has suffered a heart attack and may be dying. It would be a paralyzing experience for an uninitiated groom.

It is appropriate to describe, also, the emotional expression of this highly passionate type during intercourse and prior to its discontinuance. A large proportion of this group will whimper, emitting a sound similar to the whining a child indulges in when he is denied something. It gives the impression that the girl is in pain. Another large proportion will engage in whispered exclamations, repeating them continuously throughout the intercourse. Others will alternately ask the male to desist and proceed, being able to stand the sensation only in spurts. Others, those who thoroughly satisfy themselves, make no sounds at all but demand a continuous motion throughout. Others will dig and claw at the male back with their fingers and nails, leaving painful scratches and even drawing blood. It is impossible to have repeated relationships with such women without confining their hands, which of course limits their expression, or without wearing a heavy shirt. Many women will bite at the male mouth or breasts and will break through the skin of the hand if it is placed in their mouths to prevent even more serious damage. A large proportion will shout loudly enough to be heard throughout an apartment or private dwelling, calling upon their mother or uttering such exclamations as may occur to them as an outlet. As mentioned before, a certain percentage will shriek and scream so piercingly as to cause an investigation unless they rigidly control themselves by asking their lover to desist. Others will draw their legs back and fling them forward as if trying completely to absorb the male organ. There are women who prefer the male to penetrate slowly and deeply, some who prefer the most rapid, violent movement possible, and others who prefer early orgasm in the male because, following this, the penis loses some of its rigidity, and this practically limp state produces for them a more desirable sensation.

The size of the male organ is of no importance whatever to the vast majority of women, whether they be moderately or highly passionate. A woman is interested only in the ability of her partner to satisfy her regardless of how he may accomplish it. Nor has the size of the vaginal canal any apparent effect upon the excitement of a female. Some of the most highly passionate women are constructed with extremely wide and long canals; while many others, with vaginas almost as narrow following childbirth as before marriage, are completely devoid of sensation other than that induced in the clitoris, and are only lowly passionate.

A wide canal is no indication that a woman has consorted with numbers of men. Some canals are wide, some are narrow, some are long, and some are short. These variations do make a difference to the preferences of some men, but a male should be able to adjust himself to whatever condition exists.

A man's physical build is a matter of minor importance to most women. There are some, as has been said, who are irresistibly attracted to muscular men, and one of less prominent proportions will never stimulate them as much.

The responsiveness during intercourse of women other than the highly passionate falls into a relatively standard pattern of behavior, and varies little throughout the group. At least half are sensitive only at the clitoris, the vaginas of most being so insensitive that only the pressure of the male organ within and the sensation that the canal is filled indicates the existence of action. While the sensation of the penis moving within the vagina of the highly sensitive and even, on occasion, of the moderately sensitive, is sufficient of itself to produce orgasm, this condition alone never succeeds in creating feeling in those of the lowly sensitive group.

There is, however, a strong mental reaction to the knowledge that the penis is inserted, and this intensifies the female orgasm when it occurs. The thought that an intimate and close connection has been attained, even though no direct physical feeling exists, will heighten a climax almost doubly as against digital contact with the clitoris alone. This is just another instance of the important function the mind can play in improving sexual relationships.

With the lowly and moderately sensitive, intercourse is characterized by nothing highly emotional either in the way of speech or behavior. It is accompanied by an increasingly deep breathing; by an increased quivering which reaches its height with the climax; by the inclination of the female to increase the tempo of her genital rhythm as climax approaches; by the desire to engage in a long passionate kiss held until the orgasm occurs; and at best by muted exclamations of "oh, oh" as it does occur; although even here silence is usual unless the orgasm is extremely intense. When a long, drawn-out "oh, . . ." indicates its peak. As the sensation approaches the climax, there is also the tendency for the female to strain her body as if to increase the pressure against the clitoris or draw the penis deeper into the vagina.

This is the general behavior of the lowly and moderately sensitive during intercourse itself. There is nothing extraordinary about it, and it resembles that of the average male.

Although the majority of women sustain only one orgasm, and a great proportion none at all, the author is convinced that a husband can definitely increase the number if he goes about it properly and understands the peculiarities of the clitoris. However, since one cannot guarantee a man's efficiency in this respect, and since at the present time most women of the lowly and moderately sensitive group sustain only one climax, the situation must be spoken of as it is, not as it might be.

6.

The Type of Orgasm

UP to this point we have discussed the general conduct of intercourse. Since, as has been remarked previously, there are two types of orgastic reaction, each peculiar to the female groups under discussion, and since each group requires a different method of handling (although all groups have one feature, clitorial contact, somewhat in common), the types of orgasm will be more clearly understood if they are illustrated diagrammatically as well as explained. The type peculiar to the highly passionate group has been referred to as a sustained orgasm. In a climax of this character, the female experiences a more or less steady sensation of pleasure, enduring over a considerable period as if the crisis reached a certain height and remained there indefinitely, always producing a constant feeling of delight. It might be compared to a searchlight which, once turned on, will continue to burn until it is either deliberately extinguished by the user or until the battery becomes exhausted.

The type peculiar to the lowly and moderately sensitive group is described as an individual orgasm because the sensation does not run on indefinitely, as with the highly passionate. It reaches a peak, remains there for a relatively short period, and then automatically ceases. Like a glowing bulb, when the current is cut off, it becomes dimmer and dimmer until is disappears entirely. Following a pause by the male, it is as if the current were suddenly switched on again as soon as he resumes his efforts. If the female is capable of more than one orgasm, the crisis occurs again but reaches a lower peak. This time it is neither so long nor intense, automatically ceases, and then abates. This process repeats itself for as many climaxes as the woman is able to attain. In any case, the first is always the strongest, the peaks of the others always falling lower and lower until, finally, the male is no longer able to reinduce the sensation. The female is fully gratified.

It is perfectly possible for a woman who is capable of six individual orgasms, for example, to feel satisfied after the fourth or fifth, although she may unknowingly be capable of more. However, since the feeling is pleasurable for her at any time, there is no reason why the male should not persist in his efforts to extract from her every impulse of sensation possible before discontinuing the relationship.

The following diagrams represent the orgastic reactions of the various groups under discussion:

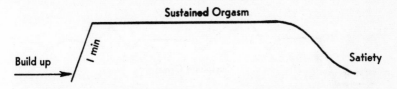

The above diagram shows the sensation building up from the low point to a peak and then flowing on steadily until the gradual decline which ends in satiety.

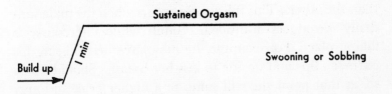

The foregoing diagram illustrates the orgasm of a woman who suddenly breaks off the intercourse either by swooning or bursting into violent tears.

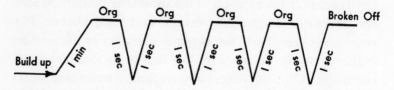

The above illustrates the reaction of a woman who requires constant interruption of the sensation. Her partner halts his activity to allow the sensation to drop completely, then reinduces it until she again calls for an interruption; this continues until she finally concludes the relationship entirely. If she could withstand continuous sensation, the diagram would be the same as the previous one. The interruptions, of course, are not as regular as those indicated on the sketch. Some may regard each interrupted phase as a distinct orgasm. Actually, this is not the case since the orgasm does not automatically discontinue itself.

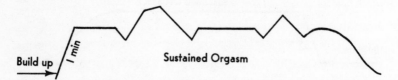

The above sketch of a sustained orgasm can be fitted into the pattern of any level. It will be observed that the flow is constant, except at two peaks. These mount higher than the others. This frequently occurs when the male suddenly introduces additional stimuli while intercourse is taking place. For example, he may have been kissing his partner's lips and decide to kiss her breasts. Should he do so, at that point she will jump to a higher peak and may even remain at that new height while the breast kissing continues, falling back to the old level as soon as it is discontinued.

On the other hand, it just as frequently happens that with the same introduction, such as breast kissing, the female will rise to a new peak and remain their only momentarily, then fall back to her old level, regardless of whether this added stimulation is continued. This is usually the case, but both possibilities have been indicated on the above diagram. It is better practice, however, to interrupt whatever suddenly lifts a woman to a higher peak, and resume it perhaps a minute later. It then comes unexpectedly, is fresh again, and will induce a new response.

When a woman rises to another peak, it can immediately detected by a deep gasp as this new and unexpected thrill bursts upon her. This is a frequent occurrence when the male, during intercourse, suddenly thrusts his penis deeper into the vagina than he has been, and presses it there for a few moments, or experiences orgasm.

The foregoing diagrams should make quite clear the nature of the orgastic reactions of a highly passionate woman. Regarding those of the other groups, however, one scheme is applicable to all, since the type of orgasm in these cases is the same. Naturally, there are varying degrees of emotion among these women as among the highly passionate. This would manifest itself with respect to the length of time it might take a woman to reach her particular peak and the length of time consumed by the orgasm itself. The former, however, is more variable than the latter. The length of time consumed by the orgasm itself probably varies little, while the length of time required for arousal can vary by many minutes. The pattern, however, is basically the same in all instances.

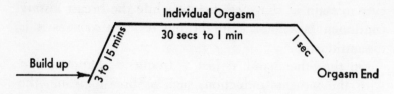

The foregoing diagram illustrates a single orgasm, the type experienced by the large majority of women. It resembles the others in appearance, but automatically cuts itself off at the end and rapidly diminishes. Unlike that of the highly emotional, the build-up time is considerably longer and the orgasm itself is of much shorter duration, as is indicated by the time set down. The length of the orgastic period and the diminishing time were omitted from the diagrams of the highly sensitive, because there is too great a variation even among these women to attempt to standardize their reactions, as can be done with the other groups. The time factors may run anywhere from three minutes.

The following represents the pattern of a woman who can experience more than one individual orgasm:

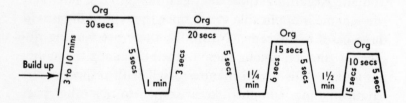

The foregoing diagram illustrates the fact that the build-up to the first orgasm is the longest but, nevertheless, shorter than those of women capable of only one orgasm. Also, the first orgasm is the most intense. When it subsides, the male must usually wait about a minute before attempting to restimulate the clitoris. Each orgasm is a complete and individual unit, entirely separate from those which precede or follow it, and each automatically terminates itself.

Following the pause, response to male inducement is immediate, orgasm being achieved in a few seconds but being less intense and less lengthy. The pauses taken by the male each time before restimulation should slightly increase, the figures set down being merely approximations and by no means representing time lapses to the precise second. However, as the orgasms increase beyond the first three, it definitely becomes necessary to lengthen the pauses by fifteen or twenty seconds each time. Apparently, the frequency begins to put a strain upon the female system after the first three orgasms, and nature consequently requires a longer period of recuperation. The build-up time also increases, and the build-up to the eighth or ninth orgasm sometimes takes as long as two minutes.

With reference to orgasms of the individual type, women experience as many as a dozen in a relationship of about forty-five minutes' duration, including foreplay; it is probable that there are females who can achieve many more. The latter, however, are definitely rare; the normal number of orgasms runs from four to ten. A woman of such intense nature is difficult to handle, as has been said before, because, in addition to other reasons subsequently explained, it is impossible to predict exactly how many climaxes she will attain. Her mood is an important factor.

An occurrence occasionally met in women of the multi-orgasm type suggests rather clearly that there is a distinct relationship between this group and the highly passionate. If it were not for the fact that nature seems deliberately to insist upon limiting the orgastic duration of the former,

both groups would in all probability be one. The following
diagram will illustrate what is meant.

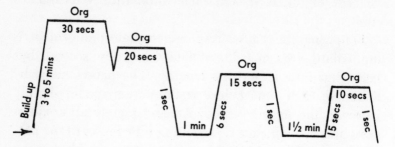

In the above it will be noted that the first orgasm does
not completely subside. The reason is that the male has
ejaculated. This has resulted in the sensation almost instantaneously reinducing itself, climbing a short distance
to a peak, and culminating in a second climax. The second
orgasm does subside, however, as do the subsequent ones.

Consequently, the first orgasm, although actually two,
is practically constant. Instead of lasting only thirty seconds, it is maintained almost a minute, the combined times
of the first and second orgasm. If we assume that this were
to occur throughout the entire cycle of a woman who
normally attains eight individual climaxes, she would
achieve what is equivalent to a sustained orgasm of approximately four minutes' duration. Such a combination
of the first two orgasms is not too frequent, nor is it infrequent. As a rule, following the jerking reaction at the end
of an orgasm, the male can continue to stimulate the
clitoris indefinitely, without reinducing sensation, if he
fails to pause in between.

It appears that individual orgasms place a greater strain
upon the nervous system of those women to whom they are
peculiar than the sustained type, and nature makes this

very clear. We know that this type of orgasm is generally the result of digital contact with the clitoris. However, once the climax has run its duration, it automatically subsides and the clitoris momentarily loses its sensitivity. This occurs regardless of whether the male continues to stimulate it. If this finger friction is maintained without pause once the climax has been reached, an involuntary and convulsive series of body jerks immediately seizes the female, warning that the orgasm has completed its course; these jerks will continue until the finger is removed from the clitoris. A subsequent orgasm cannot be achieved until this is done, and if digital contact be resumed too soon, the jerking will likewise resume.

This appears to be nature's method of informing the male that his partner's nervous system has absorbed all it can stand for the moment. A rest of a minute or so will allow the body to readjust itself and thereafter the second orgasm can be clitorally induced by the finger. When completed, this will likewise be followed by the same convulsive jerkings, whereupon another pause must be taken. With the continuation of this procedure each pause becomes longer as the orgasms increase in number, until finally, when the system has absorbed all it can stand for the moment, no amount of pause and subsequent stimulation will enable the clitoris to regain its sensitivity. Contact with it now produces only body twitches or no sensation at all. Intercourse is now completed.

Some elaboration is required regarding the pause between orgasms and other approximations. The reader will observe certain time elements marked on the diagrams. These specific times must not be taken literally. It stands to reason that one cannot prepare a timetable which will account exactly for the reactions of every woman. One can describe their reactions because, although numerous, they are limited in number. Time durations cannot be set to the absolute second. The figures given, however, will never be too far away from the reaction time of any woman now being discussed, and will give the male a sound basis for experimentation.

Further mention should be made of female body twitching; this is just as important a guide to a woman's responsiveness as is the flowing of the secretions previously mentioned. It happens sometimes that digital contact with the clitoris will result in body jerking even before the first orgasm. This immediately indicates that the female is being pressed to respond too rapidly. It is true that some fluid may be flowing, but if these jerks occur, the secretion is not yet issuing freely enough, and the clitoris is being forced to stimulation before it is ready. It can also mean that too much pressure is being placed upon it; excess pressure upon the clitoris will not only result in jerking but will also deaden sensitivity completely. It has the effect of paralyzing the nervous mechanism at that spot. The only time that excessive pressure may be placed upon the clitoris is just before the orgasm. A woman feels at that moment as if she wishes the male to push upon it and will strain her body against the finger. Even so, only a firm pressure should be used. Too much pressure, even at this point, will destroy the orgasm even though the female may believe that it will increase it. At any other time, only a light stroking will produce the best results.

It has been remarked that an incredible number of married women have never experienced an orgasm. Nothing more clearly demonstrates the ignorance of the male than his unawareness of this, because the symptoms of the female orgasm are so obvious. The difficult thing, however, is to describe the sensation to a woman who has never achieved a climax, so that she herself can give consideration to its attainment. The problem would become immediately apparent if one were asked to describe a simple headache to a person who has never experienced pain. Consequently, the sensation itself cannot be described except in terms of the sensations with which a woman is familiar in love-making. When all those which are not the orgasm are eliminated, a woman will then know that she has never attained a climax.

Let us take the analogy of a sneeze. It starts as a mild tickling sensation in the lower nostril; as one continues to inhale, the tickling builds up and changes into a sharp, pleasant sensation which seems to run up the nose into the sinuses and eyes and suddenly culminates in that delicious burst of enjoyable relief which is the sneeze. By this is not meant the sudden sneeze. Reference is made to the slow type which sometimes develops into such a lengthy paroxysm that the original pleasant sensation becomes disagreeable. If the entire sneeze, the beginning as well as the end, could be transferred to the genital region and the organs there were involved in it, the physical sensation resulting would be the closest to an orgasm as described in comparative sensations with which we are familiar.

If one prefers to regard it visually, the skyrocket makes a perfect and accurate eye picture. One sees the rocket as a flaming line mounting higher and higher until suddenly it reaches its peak, and beautiful bursts of color fly out in every direction. If it is a multiple rocket, other smaller bursts follow on lower levels, each burst diminishing until at last the sparks trail slowly down and disappear below the horizon. The individual rocket represents an individual orgasm; the multiple rocket is comparable to a series.

If one were to attempt to describe the sensation in words, it could be said that it starts with a light tickling or tingling sensation at the clitoris which gradually gathers intensity. The tingling becomes sharper and stronger until it seems to cover the entire genital area and finally culminates in a fierce burst of overwhelming, ecstatic sensation which seems to invade every organ in the genital system and is uncontrollable.

This also can be stated positively. Any woman who has ever experienced an orgasm will automatically recognize it beyond the slightest doubt. A woman who is at all uncertain has never attained it. It does not resemble and cannot be confused with any other known sensation. It is more individual and distinctive than pain; there are many types of pain, but only one sensation of orgasm. It must in all cases be felt in the genital area. It is not a sensation exclusively in either the heart or head, although the heart may pound wildly, the head may feel like bursting, and the legs may become weak from the drain upon the body's energy. The delight of the sensation is localized and experienced only in the genital area. It seems simultaneously to involve the clitoris and the interior and exterior of the vagina, and it is difficult for a woman to determine precisely whence the sensation really emanates.

It is not the sensation experienced by a woman when she is kissed by a man of whom she is passionately fond, although that feeling be magnified a thousand times. It is not the fluttering of the heart which occurs when a girl is first embraced by someone for whom she cares. It is not that hollow feeling in the stomach which arises when the legs or thighs of those physically attracted to each other meet under the table or in a crowded car. Nor is it that body hunger experienced by two people when their nakedness is merged in bed. It is a definite, unmistakable, and entirely new sensation, delirious, wild, and uncontrollable. Beyond this description, the author can add nothing more.

This is, perhaps, the appropriate point at which to take up the widely discussed simultaneous orgasm and to describe the unfortunate consequences to which it may lead. The simultaneous orgasm is attained when both parties reach their climaxes at the same time, and it is spoken of as the ultimate in sensation and as being difficult to achieve. Although it is not too often experienced consistently, anyone who observes the various methods described herein can bring it about with ease. It is usually the objective of a man who is associated with a one-orgasm woman and to whom it has never occurred to condition his partner for more than one. Since most men ignore the helpful qualities of the clitoris and stake everything upon the ability of the penis, an organ not necessarily equipped for the function it is called upon to perform; and since most women are slow in the build up, it is remarkable that any man can delay orgasm sufficiently long to meet that of his partner.

Even if a man is able to effect a simultaneous orgasm every time and with facility, what is the result? Since a man who attains his climax is not in the mood for further love-making, the possibility of his partner's ever achieving more than one orgasm is practically nonexistent. The average male's lack of conception that his partner may be capable of more than one adds to the difficulty. This pursuit of a fanciful notion will operate to maintain a woman at a single-orgasm level, a loss of completion far more to be deplored than that resulting from separate orgasms.

But even though some advocates of simultaneous orgasms also take into consideration the possibility that a woman is capable of more than one climax, they merely advise the ignorant layman to delay his orgasm without benefit of clitoral stimulation through a number of female climaxes. This is a physical impossibility as a steady activity for any man. Furthermore, these advocates fail to state specifically at what particular female orgasm the male should induce his; they merely recommend "the last."

But, who can predetermine what the last one is? The number of orgasms will definitely fluctuate from interval to interval depending upon various mental and physical factors which intrude into a woman's sex life. It is ironic, however, that the average woman is indifferent as to whether male and female climaxes are simultaneous or not. Once in the throes of an orgasm, she is more than sufficiently occupied.

With regard to the female climax, any male can tell when it is occurring, and ejaculation at any time, whether it be on a build up or during the climax itself, will heighten sensation for the female, just as if her partner were to kiss her breasts. Because of this, it is frequently assumed that since the woman is experiencing an added thrill of excitement, she is attaining her climax and that the orgasms are occurring simultaneously. On the contrary, she has been experiencing orgasms all along and will still continue to experience them on the former level if her partner maintains his efficiency, which is unlikely. What frequently happens is that the male, observing the jump in emotion his partner has taken as his ejaculation occurs, assumes she is also reaching her climax and is now ready to subside, as he is. Naturally, the moment he relaxes, he discontinues the friction necessary for his partner's sensation, and she subsides prematurely—rarely to admit, no matter how often it occurs, that she has the capacity to continue. This is another of the complications which may arise from concentrating on simultaneity.

Since the male orgasm at any time will heighten a woman's sensation, it makes not the slightest difference to most females when he experiences it, so long as he makes certain his partner is not denied her full complement of pleasure. There is only one time he can be certain of this and that is after she has reached her capacity for that intercourse.

As a further consideration, from the standpoint of direct physical sensation, the simultaneous climax adds nothing at all in a large proportion of cases. While a man can easily detect orgasm in his partner, it is frequently impossible for the woman to detect the male climax, since it depends largely upon the nature of the man and his responsiveness. Many man are completely taut at the moment of orgasm, and it is only when the sensation is occurring and subsiding that they relax and start breathing deeply, thus evincing the only symptom that climax has been achieved. Furthermore, should either partner be employing some contraceptive device, the woman cannot feel the spurting of the semen, especially if her vagina is relatively or completely insensitive. She can determine the male's climax only by the depth of his breathing, by his exclamations, or perhaps by the tightening of his arms about her; this translates itself into a mental conception which heightens the physical. Since she may feel nothing at all within the vagina, the male orgasm is useless in a great percentage of instances as a direct vaginal stimulant.

There are, however, some women who will demand a simultaneous orgasm. These women are members of the highly passionate group to whom male responsiveness is more important than with any other. Theirs is an attitude not common to women in general. They are tremendously moved by the thought that they have been able to produce a moment of intense pleasure for their lover, and this is combined with the realization that he is deeply enjoying them as the instrument thereof. This results in a tremendous physical thrill which, however pleasurable to them at any time, is particularly so at a certain peak of their climax. Such women will usually exclaim to their lover in terms of endearment such as a mother might use to a child who has fallen and hurt himself. Since such women form a small proportion of the highly passionate group, to the majority of whom the moment of male orgasm is of small consequence, their tastes are an insufficient criterion on which to base a recommended procedure for the majority.

It might be added, also, that few lovers, particularly women, have a desire to carry on a constant conversation when involved in sexual throes. However, unless both parties continue to inquire concerning their mutual progress toward orgasm, simultaneity will hardly be achieved. Automatic timing is not consistently possible. Furthermore, there is always the reluctance of each to be the first to attain climax. This results in physical and mental effort on the part of both to merge orgasms, and interferes with the smoothness of intercourse. Notwithstanding, the male orgasm usually precedes that of the female and, where the timing is close, causes the female climax to follow immediately. Even this is not true simultaneity but approximate, the former under any circumstances being rarely attained.

Everything taken into consideration, it would be of greater practical value for a husband to concentrate upon a technique which aims to extend the pleasure of his wife rather than shorten it.

It might be wondered, since the orgasm is a sensation which all of us experience, why it affects some people more intensely than others. Is the quality itself any deeper in one individual than in another?

The author believes that the quality of orgasm is of the same intensity for all, though not necessarily of the same duration. Its effect depends entirely upon the make-up of a person, as well as the length of climax. With respect to duration, a woman of the individual-orgasm type enjoys a shorter experience of sensation than does a woman who sustains a prolonged climax. The shorter period experienced by the former allows her no time to become expressive in her passion. It is there one moment and gone the next. But even throughout its short interval, a female is uncontrollably and violently convulsed. If her orgasm were prolonged, it is possible and probable that she would react precisely as her highly passionate sisters, because she would have sufficient time for it.

A needle jabbed an eighth of an inch into a person's thumb and instantly withdrawn, will result in a sharp twinge of pain. But the same needle, jabbed the same distance and allowed to remain, will create unbearable pain. All the factors are the same but in the latter case a cumulative effect builds up over the longer period. Duration has a decided bearing upon intensity.

Individual make-up has equal importance with duration. It is a combination of the two which determines the varied responses encountered in the sex act. For example, a hundred volts of electricity hurled at various people will not necessarily affect them all the same way. Some may faint, some will undergo a greater contraction of the muscles, some may be knocked flat. But it is only one hundred volts. This may be called "individual predisposition." In connection with pain, the thresholds of individuals vary, although the identical measure is applied to all. Logic would suggest that similar relationships apply to the pleasure of intercourse. Some women and men simply react differently to the same degree of pleasure.

Regarding the degree of sexual emotion, sexology is still debating the old question as to which of the sexes is the more passionate. It is difficult to see how there can be doubt as to the answer. A highly passionate woman can be reduced to a state where she is physically unable to protest, so completely is she overwhelmed by her desire. Should man sustain a prolonged orgasm, such as is achieved by the highly passionate type of woman, it is probable that he, also, might faint or burst into tears. Many men, as it is, sob violently. But because most of the male sex do not, conditions must be compared as they are.

Since woman generally has the capacity to experience more than one orgasm, since many do, and since some can attain a continuous climax of long duration, the male, who is always limited to a single culmination, definitely experiences his climax in a lesser quantity, even though the initial intensity of both may be identical. Since, also, capacity is the measure that determines the quantity of anything, and since the female sustains a greater number of orgasms, it follows that she must have a greater capacity for passion and is, therefore, more passionate. The fact that she requires a longer period for satisfaction adds further support.

Consequently, in any sexual relationship, man may be regarded as the master of the situation. It remains for him to live up to his responsibility.

7.

The Importance of Digital Contact

IT may be wondered, since the penis is reputed to be the primarily effective sexual organ of the male, why the author stresses the importance of finger contact with the clitoris in producing the female orgasm. The sad fact is that, from a practical standpoint, the penis is only one of the instruments creating sensation in the female, and its greatest value lies as a mental stimulant and organ of reproduction, not as a necessary medium of her sexual pleasure. The truth is that even as a reproductive organ it is not indispensable; many women have been artificially inseminated.

Although the penis is regarded as the sole conveyer of pleasure for the female, the disillusioning fact remains that the forefinger is a most useful asset in man's contact with the opposite sex, and that the highly vaunted male organ requires much assistance as an instrument of woman's sexual pleasure.

It is time that this matter was faced. It is insistence on making the penis do something it cannot generally do that is responsible for a major proportion of sexual incompatibility. Also, it is difficult to believe that nature intended the penis to be the sole instrument of pleasure for women. She created both male and female with desire, then made it necessary for the male to obtain his satisfaction by inserting his organ within the recesses of a woman. Once it was there, nature apparently realized that the male would persist until ejaculation occurred; nature thus achieved her objective. If the woman obtained any pleasure as a by-product, well and good. If not, it was simply unfortunate.

Consequently, it is the author's opinion that whatever is done as the result of man's personal wish to intensify the pleasure of intercourse for a woman must be done with little co-operation on nature's part.

To satisfy many women, a man must resort to artificial stimulation; a normal penis and a normal clitoris cannot as a rule contact each other. When it is said that the penis and clitoris cannot contact each other, it is meant that they cannot do so with any degree of comfort or convenience to the male, or with any hope of satisfactory intercourse. If the penis is fully inserted in the vagina, it is nowhere near the clitoris; the penis is entirely within, and the clitoris is entirely without. In order to retain its position in the vagina and at the same time contact the clitoris, the penis must be arched almost into a backward semi-circle. Accomplishing this represents a form of torture.

Even assuming it could be achieved with infinite pleasure, a small penis would slip completely out of the vagina; only a portion of the head could remain inside, and full movement, always retaining contact with the clitoris, would allow the male organ to enter the canal little more than an inch. An inch in a straining position against lubricated walls would allow no purchase whatever, and the penis would invariably slip out. Even if we assume the contrary, what pleasure is involved for either party in utilizing only one inch of a canal perhaps three inches in length? If the tip of the clitoris were larger than it is, the problem would be immeasurably reduced. However, such a condi-

tion in a woman is a rare abnormality and usually necessitates an operation. Constant friction imposed against it
by walking or tight clothing would keep her in a state of
continuous excitement.

Consequently, since constant clitoral contact, or even
any clitoral contact, with the penis is a rare possibility;
and since with most women clitoral friction is necessary
to produce sensation, there remains but one agency in intercourse—the finger. Of course, perfect clitoral contact
with the male organ can be established if no attempt is
made to penetrate the vagina. In this case, the male organ
remains completely outside and extends past the vaginal
entrance, coming in contact only with the external genitals. This will produce orgasm in both the female and the
male, but it is not perfect intercourse; that vital mental
element of true intimacy is lacking for the man unless he
controls his orgasm until after his partner has been satisfied, and then attains it in the normal way. This is the
manner in which many young girls and women preserve
their hymen, but not their chastity. Furthermore, a woman
lacks the same mental satisfaction because, whether her
orgasm is caused digitally or not, she prefers to feel the
male organ nestling within her.

One might conclude that, although digital contact with
the clitoris involves the majority of women, there still remain a substantial number, the highly passionate, for
whom digital contact may be held to a minimum or ignored completely on the ground that the entire internal
and external genital region is supersensitively independent
of the clitoris. Unfortunately, that conclusion is arrived at
only by completely ignoring the facts.

In the first place, most men married to highly passionate
women are not necessarily more informed than those mar-

ried to other types. One might almost assume that the majority of men know more about the appendix than they do about the clitoris. Those involved with highly passionate women have even less reason to know, because practically any spot they touch within the genital area is sensitive, and they have little cause especially to search for the clitoris. They know also that their partners go into all manner of ecstasies as soon as the penis is inserted; they know, too, that their ejaculation produces a rise in the emotions of their partners, and they frequently assume she is enjoying her only orgasm.

In this connection there are women who will react violently whether the male orgasm occurs at the beginning of the intercourse or at the end. There are others who, when for reasons of safety it becomes necessary for the male to withdraw, will ask that the semen be ejected on their abdomen or their leg. When this occurs, they will frequently rise to a greater pitch of excitement than when the orgasm occurs within them. That does not, however, indicate that they are attaining their only climax. They remain excited considerably longer, but their stimulation must be continued by the finger, since it is disagreeable for the average man to persist too long in intercourse once he has ejaculated.

All this, combined with the fact that most women will not induce a partner to continue once he has experienced his climax and shows signs of lack of interest, has resulted in the impression that complete satisfaction is always achieved by the highly passionate type through the agency of the penis alone. This conception, of course, is incorrect. It is possible to satisfy a woman solely with the penis, as will be explained. Unfortunately, however, not every man has developed the necessary self-control and not every man favors the position advised to assist it. Even under ideal conditions, there arise situations in which no man has the power to delay his orgasm. The only answer is digital contact with the clitoris or other genitals. It might be added, too, that with respect to the highly passionate, the region of stimulation makes little difference; it may be the clitoris, the vulva in general, or the vaginal interior. However, despite the satisfactory sensitivity of the entire area, the clitoris will nevertheless always produce the strongest sensation in a woman. From any viewpoint, the male organ plays only a supporting role.

There are three effective methods by which the clitoris may be stimulated digitally. One is by moving the tip of the finger quickly, but lightly and uninterruptedly, over the tip of the clitoris. This will cause a more rapid stimulation and is best used only when the clitoris is sluggish or when the male wishes to bring on an orgasm rapidly.

The second method is to run the forefinger from tip to base, as previously described, over the entire clitoris, entering the vagina with the finger and then withdrawing, returning again in the same manner, just as the penis would normally do, if it were possible. These strokes, slow, deep, and regular, will induce the best quality of sensation into the rise-and-fall technique, and will produce a sensation similar to that induced by the penis, were it able to behave in this manner.

The third method is to avoid the tip of the clitoris completely and partially encircle it with the tip of the finger, running the finger back and forth over the buried portion as if tracing the letter "U." The male starts a little below the clitoris, alongside and within the small lips, brings his finger up and around the base and down the other side, retracing the same pattern and doing it repeatedly. By interspersing this with the second method, an enjoyable variety of sensation for the female can be introduced into the build-up.

This thought must always be kept in mind by the male who has never concerned himself with the clitoris. This organ may not respond with sensation immediately upon contact, and it very definitely will not respond if the lubricating fluid is not flowing. If, however, proper attention has been given to foreplay, and the female is not in an unfavorable mood, the fluid will be flowing sufficiently to permit concentration upon the clitoris.

Nevertheless, a woman who is slow to respond or one who has never experienced the orgasm may not, and probably will not, develop a sensation at the clitoris within the first minute or two. This does not mean that the female will not respond. It is far from rare to be forced to stimulate the clitoris for as long as five minutes before sensation starts to develop; with a woman who has never experienced orgasm, twenty minutes to three-quarters of an hour is a normal length of time to devote to developing this necessary phase of enjoyment. With these common situations to contend with, it should be quite clear that under no circumstances could a man ever expect to bring about a female orgasm by the conventional use of the male organ.

This slow condition in a woman must always be met with persistence and male determination to conquer this disinterest on nature's part. It can be conquered—but not by the penis. Furthermore, once a woman experiences a sensation or orgasm with constancy and frequency, additional climaxes will definitely follow, because a psychological factor has been removed and the woman knows she is perfectly normal. Some women can enjoy love-making for hours, can remain perfectly relaxed, can be touched anywhere on the body, can entertain no aversion to sex, can have children, and yet never attain a climax or perhaps have attained only one in their entire sexual life. Once they experience regular orgasms, however, the period reduces itself to normalcy.

In all these situations of lengthy clitorial stimulation, the male must be prepared to use artificial lubricants. Of course, sexual feeling between the partners must also exist. If this is the case and the woman is not frigid, it is most unlikely that she will fail eventually to enjoy a normal sex life.

8.

The Technique of Coitus

A T this point, a word of warning must be given regarding foreplay. While this preliminary is usually underextended, it can also be overdone, particularly where the woman is not disposed to interfere with what she regards as pleasurable to the male. There is a limit, of course, to a woman's excitement, and it is characteristic of foreplay that, after a reasonable period of indulgence, the female level of high emotion is reached. Since no new element can now be added to increase it except intercourse, it remains stationary. If foreplay is continued too long thereafter, the woman's excitement begins to abate and she starts to cool. This will be attended immediately by a natural diminishing of the lubricating fluid. Since intercourse is always to be preceded by devoting a certain amount of time adequately to stimulating the clitoris and vulva generally, even with the highly passionate, the hand will immediately detect a reduction in the flow of the secretion; the area begins to dry fairly rapidly. There will be a noticeable change in the texture of the moistness which, in addition to becoming less abundant, will also lose its slickness and become definitely thin and watery. The male should then enter into intercourse immediately.

This cooling is only occasional with a highly passionate woman, since it is difficult to over-provide her with indulgence. It occurs most frequently with women of lower emotional levels; since they are more speedily satisfied, excessive foreplay serves as an outlet for their emotion, and they may start cooling prior to orgasm.

When the male feels that sufficient foreplay has taken place, fifteen minutes being the minimum unless otherwise directed by the female, he can then turn to intercourse. He will discover that his partner responds to it immediately. However, there is nothing mechanical about a sexual relationship, and it is the male's habit of treating it as such which causes much dissatisfaction and may ultimately drive the wife to someone who takes it more seriously.

In developing this view, let us start with the highly passionate and consider first the impediments to their full satisfaction. We know that these women are quickly aroused and that they have the capacity to enjoy a lengthy foreplay, although it is not necessary, and to experience a lengthy orgasm. We know, too, that the male is quick to experience orgasm, which is of short duration, and quick to abate in excitement. We know further that, unless a woman is completely satisfied, the result can be irritation and even suffering, neither of which is conducive to a happy married life. It follows, then, that regardless of his feelings, capacities, or abilities, all restricted by nature, it is man's duty to satisfy his mate.

Since such a female has the capacity to enjoy a lengthy foreplay, he must sustain it. In order to do this, he must refrain from any excessive activity involving the penis lest he induce an orgasm in himself. Necessarily, therefore, he must employ largely his mouth and hands. Women in the highly passionate group are thrown into ecstasies by alternate kissing of the mouth and breast and by the hands simultaneously passing over the outside and inside of the thighs, brought up to the groin, and brought down again halfway to the knee. Only occasionally should the hands move lightly but firmly over the vulva to give the clitoris a soft but lengthy passing stroke. When the entire finger is passed over the clitoris, from tip to base, such a stroke is characteristic of the behavior of the penis. The male should vary this procedure by placing his leg between both of his partner's and rubbing it up and down over the vulva. This, of course, creates a friction upon that area, which is sensitive throughout; many women utilize this contact, leaving the penis unagitated.

In his relations with any woman, a man may employ a variety of stimuli, and can absorb much of his enjoyment from his partner's excitation and the knowledge that he is the agency controlling it. Unless she is the type to desire an early insertion of the penis or unless she has some personal procedure which she enjoys, the type of foreplay just described can be extended indefinitely.

Highly passionate women are affected by the male organ to an extent unapproached by any other type. They enjoy pressing it between their breasts, fondling it, and kissing it. With regard to the latter, it is a rare man who fails to enjoy this attention and who will not be moved to orgasm by an excess of it. A very few men, however, do not care for such intimacy. While the vast majority of highly passionate woman have an intense desire for oral contact with the penis, most will restrain themselves from a mistaken sense of decency unless encouraged by their partners, a good percentage of whom set no example from a like fear of offending the female.

There is absolutely nothing abnormal about this form of indulgence. It is a natural urge; it is engaged in by more couples than is suspected; and in Europe is a common practice. Since the lay mind associates everything of an erotic character with France, and because it is presumed to have had its birth in some remote French province, this practice has come to be known as the "French Method," although it is no more common in France than elsewhere. The prejudice against it exists largely among the lower class, whose males, unfortunately, represent the most inadequate lovers of any caste. A subsequent chapter is devoted to a discussion of this behavior.

Once a man engages in intercourse, he can, if there is no interruption in the rhythm, attain orgasm within a few minutes. But, whether a woman experiences an individual or a sustained orgasm and whether she be lowly or highly passionate, it will take her considerably longer. How much longer depends upon the sexual nature of the woman, but it is unquestionable that it will positively exceed the time of the male under any circumstances. Consequently, the husband, if he would prolong the pleasure for his partner, cannot follow his normal inclination. Obviously he must reduce his rhythm; however, since sensation for his partner depends upon a continuous flow, stimulation must be effected by some means other than the penis. The sensation of the male organ lying restfully within the vagina, while pleasurable, is not ecstatically so and will never produce orgasm by inactivity.

Should the motion be slow and deep each time the penis comes to a rest, a drop in sensation will result in the highly passionate female, who prefers it to remain constant. Unlike the lowly and moderately sensitive she can experience the sensation at a high level for a considerable length of time. It is pointless to induce a rise and fall of feeling in such a woman when she is capable of experiencing much more. There is a definite place for the "rise-and-fall" technique, but it is not the method employed in satisfying a highly passionate woman.

Even a slow deep rhythm will ultimately produce orgasm in the male, because his own pitch rises higher with each movement until it culminates in the climax. Also, his partner, in order to maintain the sensation, will herself engage in motion which affects him in any pause he may make; this, too, is likely to result in ejaculation for the male. Normally, then, he has four choices if he wishes to wring from the relationship the last measure of pleasure for his partner; he can either allow her to do all the work from an above position; he can proceed with his orgasm and thereafter force himself to continue the motion, whether with the penis or finger, until his partner is satisfied; he can delay inserting himself and stimulate her digitally both by means of the clitoris and other genitalia until she is almost satisfied and then proceed normally with his own orgasm; or he can insert himself, keep the penis at rest, and stimulate her digitally at the clitoris, making occasional thrusts with the penis until such time as he judges appropriate for his own climax.

Now these are specific methods by which any normal man, whatever his degree of control, can feel certain that he has not only satisfied his partner but has prolonged her pleasure to its fullest extent and has done it in a perfectly normal fashion. Furthermore, a man cannot adopt any other procedure and guarantee the outcome. Those husbands who find themselves hard-pressed to meet the demands of the highly sensitive group will discover that the foregoing offers a pracitcal variety of successful technique.

All other types of woman fall into one category—the individual orgasm group. At least half are sensitive only at the clitoris, and the remainder, although moderately sensitive elsewhere, are not sufficiently so to alter the problem involved or the general procedure. From the standpoint of adequate handling by the male, they represent no actual difficulty, because there is only one simple way to proceed. Also, since most of these women experience only one orgasm, and many none at all, one need concern himself solely with producing orgasm in those who have never achieved it and with increasing the number of climaxes for those who have.

It is a fact that any woman who is not frigid and is physically and mentally normal is capable of orgasm. A frigid woman is one who, while not perverted, finds the sex act disagreeable with all men. If a woman is frigid toward one man, but not toward others, she does not fall into this classification, since she is capable of orgasm with the object of her desire. In other words, if a woman enjoys kissing and being kissed and is capable of desire, she is also capable of orgasm. If she has the capacity for one, she has it for more, the number depending both upon her nature and her mood. Consequently, it is safe to assume that any normal woman is capable of at least two, and the majority of at least three. It is also probable that the use of a proper technique can operate to further increase the number.

It has been said that there is only one simple way to proceed with women of the individual orgasm type. Since their climax is not long sustained, one must inject as much pleasure as possible in developing it. Furthermore, at least half of such women are sensitive only at the clitoris. Therefore, it is necessary for the male to direct his attention only to this spot.

Such women also have the added characteristic of being slow to arouse; this holds true even of those who can achieve more than one climax. Although they respond more rapidly to stimulation, they are relatively slow by comparison with the highly passionate. It is practicable to consider them in the same category as the others in discussing procedure.

The climax achieved by such women is of short duration. Consequently, much of their pleasure must be crowded into the first part of the actual intercourse, the development of the orgasm. This is achieved only by the "rise-and-fall" technique. Although an incredible number of women have never experienced the sensation of orgasm, it will be expedient to proceed as if the sensation of climax could be achieved by all.

Those who have attained it are familiar with the constantly rising sensation of pleasure which starts in the genital area, specifically at the clitoris and, if not interrupted, builds to the orgasm. Since the orgasm is nothing more than this sensation at its apex, even its start is naturally not without intense enjoyment. The rise-and-fall technique consists of bringing the sensation to the point just before it explodes into the orgasm, then breaking it off, allowing it to descend of its own accord, and then repeating the process either until the woman begins to cool or until she expresses a desire for the climax.

Since half the group is sensitive only to clitoral stimulation, and since the clitoris is also the strongest center of sensation in the other half, it is essential to concentrate upon this organ. Because the clitoris generally can be contacted by the penis only with the greatest discomfort, if at all, the only practical instrument with which to induce sensation is the finger, with the penis occupying a place of secondary importance as a physical stimulant and of primary importance as a mental one.

Even those women who have no sexual feeling whatever within the vagina are excited by the introduction of the male organ. Although its entrance produces absolutely no sensation, the knowledge that one of the most intimate of positions exists is sufficient to create an upsurge of passion, and an orgasm by the female under such conditions is more intense than if induced merely by the finger itself. Consequently, the female orgasm and part of the build-up to it should always take place with the penis inserted, regardless of how much pre-clitoral stimulation was induced digitally.

The proper procedure to create the greatest amount of pleasure for the female, both in length of time and intensity, is to start inducing the rise and fall of sensation exclusively by the finger. It is not difficult to determine the point just beyond which the female orgasm will occur. As sensation increases the woman begins to vibrate and to raise the genital area gradually as if to establish a greater contact between the clitoris and the finger.

Although she feels that the greater the pressure, the greater will be the intensity of the sensation, she does not realize that too great a pressure will have the opposite effect. The same pressure which induced the sensation from the beginning is to be maintained throughout. As she raises the genitals, and the vibrations become of a quivering nature, the stroking of the clitoris should be interrupted immediately, whereupon she will sink back to her original position. As soon as this has occurred, the procedure should be repeated at once; this time, it will be observed that the sensation develops almost instantaneously, that it is much stronger, and that she vibrates and raises the genital region more pronouncedly than before.

Clitoral contact is again interrupted, and a longer pause
ensues. If the contact stages follow each other too closely,
she will attain orgasm. The male's sole purpose is to create
as many of these up-and-down sensations as possible without carrying them so far as to bring about a climax. The
first pause should approximate five seconds; the second
eight seconds; the third, ten seconds; the fourth, twelve
seconds.

After perhaps the fifth rise, the male may allow a substantial interruption of about a minute or a minute and a
half, this time allowing his partner thoroughly to subside.
Thereafter he can re-initiate this routine, always watching for signs of cooling. Then, following ten or fifteen of
such responses, it is appropriate to introduce the penis and
engage in the conventional in-and-out rhythm which will
gradually bring the male to the same stage of excitement
as his partner. Should the man be the active type and
should the woman be moderately sensitive throughout the
vulva, digital contact with the clitoris may be abandoned.
Should the woman be sensitive only at the clitoris, the
man must continue to stimulate it because, regardless of
the movement made by the male organ, absolutely no
physical sensation will be induced in the vagina by the
penis alone.

Once the man is situated within his partner, the couple
may then experience orgasm as it appeals to them. The
female will now feel less inclined to prolong the act, and
the orgasms may be achieved simultaneously or separately,
as the couple wish. Either way, such intercourse is perfect,
with both attaining climax, and the woman having enjoyed a pre-period of pleasurable stimulation. Under conditions involving women of the type now being described,

this is the only proper and practicable manner in which to conduct intercourse which will be certain to satisfy the female.

Digital contact with the clitoris should always be carefully maintained. This is most important, because the height, frequency, and quality of the rise-and-fall sensation, as well as the intensity of the orgasm, is completely dependent upon the character of the contact exerted by the finger. Too firm a pressure will definitely decrease the sensation, if not destroy it completely. Too light a contact, though far better than too heavy, will not develop the sensation to its fullest intensity. The contact must be firm enough to trace practically the entire clitoris from the area lying just beneath the surface to the tip.

The tip of an erected clitoris, being unprotected by its sheath, is ultra-sensitive. For that reason it may occur that a direct touch upon it will produce at times an involuntary body-jerking on the part of the female. When this happens, attention should be directed at its base and at least a half minute to a minute allowed before again attempting to contact the tip itself. Experience will develop the precise technique.

Since the intercourse has now been discussed in detail, it is well to enlarge upon a matter previously referred to, the possibility of increasing the number of individual climaxes for a woman. Any woman who is capable of one climax is capable of several, for generally a single orgasm is not too severe a drain upon the female nervous system. It does not last sufficiently long to tax it, and is not accompanied by the loss of vital fluid or the strain upon the manufacturing processes of that fluid which attends the male climax. Since the orgastic reaction of all men is practically identical, and since it varies so extensively in women, it cannot be intended that it should impose a greater strain upon some than others, but rather that it should express itself differently with different women. Regardless of the past sexual experience of a normal woman, there is generally room for improvement.

This problem, of course, involves only women of low responsiveness, those whose stimulative capacities lie largely at the clitoris. It has been previously explained how to conduct intercourse properly with such a type. But it is to be emphasized that the male must delay his orgasm until he is certain that the woman has achieved her ultimate climax or that she has been sufficiently satisfied to wish to conclude the relationship. The male determines that the final orgasm has been achieved by continuing to stimulate the clitoris. If, following a minute or so of this procedure, the female fails to respond as previously, or is seized with a series of body-jerkings, he should ask her if she still experiences sensation there. If the answer is negative, the woman is satisfied.

However, there are occasions when a man will have difficulty restimulating a woman following a prior orgasm; when she will assert upon questioning that the sensation has disappeared; but when persistence on his part may result in a renewal of sensation and the occurrence of several additional orgasms. This condition usually exists in the early stages, after the second or third climax. But should it occur after the fourth or fifth, the male may conclude that the woman is satisfied, although it will do no harm to persist for another minute. It is to be remembered that clitoral stimulation should be discontinued immediately and a pause taken whenever a woman exhibits the jerking, twitching movements previously referred to.

In striving to increase the capacity of a one-orgasm

woman, the male must delay his orgasm until she has experienced her first climax. This is not difficult. The relationship is conducted with the customary observance of foreplay and the build-up to the orgasm by means of the rise-and-fall technique. When he decides that the time is propitious for the first female orgasm, the male inserts himself as deeply as possible, pressing his genital region tightly against that of his partner, holding this position, and maintaining a constant digital contact with the clitoris. His object now is to bring on the female orgasm as rapidly as possible. He will observe also that the female exerts a similar pressure against him. As soon as the first female orgasm has occurred, he should discontinue digital contact at the first manifestation of the body-jerking. He must reduce the pressure of the male organ, allowing it to assume a more relaxed position in the vagina, and wait at least thirty seconds before attempting to induce a second climax.

The second and all subsequent orgasms should be developed much in the same manner as the first, but without resort to the rise-and-fall procedure. This is used only in connection with the build-up to the first orgasm. It is difficult enough to induce subsequent climaxes without placing an additional strain upon them, and all future orgasms should be brought about as rapidly as possible. The penis should again penetrate as deeply as it can, but the male should maintain an increasing pressure as if trying to enter further and further, and at the same time agitate the tip of the clitoris, with the finger moving unceasingly and as rapidly as possible. Should his partner suddenly be seized with body-jerking, he should reduce the pressure of the forefinger, discontinue the stimulation for twenty-five or thirty seconds, and then proceed as before. The second orgasm will not last so long as the former nor be so intense; the first is usually the strongest, the remainder becoming shorter and weaker, although remaining pleasurable.

In summary, the four principal and necessary elements in inducing additional orgasms above one, are to bring them on as quickly as possible, to maintain constant digital contact, to make the finger movement as rapid as possible, and to exert genital pressure against the female genitals.

Since access to the clitoris by the finger is more difficult when the genital areas are pressed firmly together, it is best to experiment the first few times with the male organ lying outside the vagina. Induce the first orgasm by digital means exclusively, maintaining the contact as long as the climax endures. When it shows a tendency to subside, allow it to do so, wait a half minute, and then repeat the process. The partner should ask if the female experiences any build-up sensation. It she does, even though it cannot be brought to an immediate climax, the couple know that subsequent orgasms are not only possible but probable, and that later relationships will produce them. If difficulty is experienced with the penis lying outside the vagina, it should be inserted. The female may need just that added mental stimulus to achieve a climax. It frequently happens that such women, while experiencing the build-up sensation, cannot be brought to a climax without the introduction of the penis, although most females can be induced to multiple orgasms by the finger alone. However, no climax will ever be as intense for a woman, although it may be for a man, as when the male organ lies within the vagina.

Notwithstanding all that has been said with respect to the lowly sensitive or those whose sensitivity is located exclusively in the clitoris, time offers a hopeful possibility to partners who are patient. It frequently occurs that after many years of constant association, a woman who previously required digital stimulation to attain a climax, may suddenly respond to the penis.

There are actually two elements concerned in this transition: technique and deepening affection. When two persons—whose life together has been satisfactory—advance in years, a strong bonding agent develops and cements their ties more closely together. Various factors influence this, of which the strongest is habit. A man who is accustomed to returning from work each evening and finding a neat wife with a pleasant smile and a warm kiss, has no reason or desire to avoid his home. In fact, he looks forward to this nightly reunion. Should he feel in an amorous mood, he knows beforehand that a period of lovemaking will be just as welcome to his wife. At least, incompatibility doesn't add to his normal outside problems.

Can the average woman see her importance and responsibility in this domestic picture? Can she see the contrast in a scene wherein a husband is greeted by an untidy, nagging shrew whose complaints begin as soon as he crosses the threshold? Can she see that it is largely up to her to keep the matrimonial ship on an even keel?

Of course, many women will rise in protest and argue, "Well, how about the duties of a husband? Supposing he arrives ready for an argument? What are we supposed to do, take it?"

Certainly. A wife is supposed to take it. If it were intended that she fight back like another man, she might as well be one. A woman was meant to be soft and flexible, not a battling Amazon. A man is attracted by a woman's gentleness; not by the qualities of a spit-fire. The world has always been too full of male hostility. That's what is wrong with it— man's inhumanity to man. Any woman who seeks to justify her participation in it, is seriously lacking in feminine virtue. During time of war a woman's role is primarily that of a comforter. No man would care to see her shouldering a rifle. It would be out of place. And her belligerence is equally out of place in the home.

It must be remembered that only in fairly recent years have women been competing so extensively with men, assuming their place in the world. And never has the divorce rate been higher. Originally, the home and the rearing of her children were her principal responsibilities. The problem of providing the daily bread belonged to the man. It was an excellent and practical arrangement. While she may have been physically tired at the end of the day, it was recognized that the physical and mental problems concerned with earning a living were the more exhausting.

Consequently, one of her wifely duties was to provide for the male comfort and relaxation. In fact, in the old world that is still the fashion, even among women of wealth and station. Basically, despite the release from drudgery brought about by modern methods, it still remains one of her primary functions. The woman who feels that she is entitled to yell back at a grouchy husband, is simply unwomanly. She is a misfit in the natural order of things.

True, it might be annoying to greet with a smile a sullen, disagreeable mate. But if she possesses the feminine tact about which she will probably boast, and forget about the philosophy of equal rights, she can manage to soothe his irritation and eventually work him around to an amiable frame of mind. A clever wife can and will do this.

Naturally, this does not refer to some surly, loud-mouthed brute who immediately upon entering the house pours forth vicious abuse or slams his way from room to room. Any wife who remains with such a man for a protracted period, regardless of economic necessity, deserves whatever mistreatment she receives. Reference is made only to a husband who may be quarrelsome on occasion as the result of outside aggravations. For a woman to reciprocate will not improve the situation at all. It can only make it worse. An intelligent wife realizes this and assumes the task of improving his mood. If he is a reasonable man, she will succeed. Otherwise, she maintains a judicious silence and waits for his irritability to pass.

A home life based upon this type of womanly and wifely consideration, must eventually produce firm compatibility. As the years pass, constancy draws the couple closer and closer together until an unbreakable structure, solidly cemented with love, is erected. Meanwhile, the children are growing up, and the parents know them for another link binding the marriage even more securely. The husband reflects upon his wife's uncomplaining cooperation in the past and realizes he has been, indeed, blessed. The wife recalls his struggles to provide her with comfort and security, and is also grateful. At this point, love reaches its full maturity.

It is, now, when mutual devotion is at its highest level, that the transition previously referred to, takes place. Being a woman of a lowly sensitive sexual nature, her climaxes throughout the past necessitated digital stimulation of the clitoris, entirely, to bring them about. Her husband, properly, had always utilized this technique with the male organ inserted. Every two or three months, perhaps, he would attempt to induce his wife's orgasm by means of penis rhythm alone but never succeeded. Then, one night, for no apparent reason, the ultimate occurs. His wife attains the majority of her climaxes without benefit of digital stimulation. From then on, it becomes a fairly consistent happening, not always to be fully relied upon, but probable during four out of five relationships.

In considering the technique to be employed, it must be emphasized that complete digital stimulation of the clitoris can never be abandoned. The woman is still a member of the lowly sensitive group and will always remain one. Digital contact is vital, at least, to bring such a wife to the point of orgasm. Let us examine the procedure involved in this situation step by step.

First of all, the proper divisions of foreplay must be carefully observed with a lowly sensitive woman. As has been set down, during the first half of foreplay the husband ignores the genitals almost completely and devotes himself to the other areas of the female body. He may, however, if he thinks it necessary, lay his right leg between those of his wife, and by moving it up and down attempt to generate some friction in his partner's genital zone. He may even spread the lips of the vulva with his fingers so that his leg lays directly upon the membrane rather than the epidermis of the lips. Beyond this, there is no hand contact directly with the genital area during the first half of foreplay.

It should be mentioned also, that unless a man is left handed, preliminary love making should always be conducted from the right side of a woman. This gives the corresponding hand of the male—the hand that operates with better advantage—complete freedom.

The second half of foreplay concerns itself with digital excitation of the clitoris. During this phase, if a husband is doubtful of his wife's progress, she should be asked to tell him when she is ready to experience the orgasm. Since she knows her precise state of emotion, she usually remarks at the appropriate moment, "I can have it any time now."

Since the husband is dealing with a multi-orgasm woman (in past years, he has conditioned her to attain more than one climax), he ignores the "rise and fall" technique and inserts himself from the "man above" position. The shifting of the bodies necessary to assume this, forces him to abandon the clitoris, as a result of which his partner's emotion drops to some degree. Normally, this readjustment would have made it necessary for him to re-stimulate the clitoris, perhaps, for another minute from the new position until his wife achieved her previous level of excitation and was again prepared for orgasm. Now, however, he ignores this organ and penetrates the vagina as deeply as possible. He allows the penis to remain there, and holds both pubic regions firmly together. Maintaining this contact, he attempts to revolve the penis in a circular motion.

If his wife is ready for the transition, an increasing level of emotion that he recognizes as a new element is her reactions, clearly manifests itself. Withdrawing and re-entering slowly, he repeats the previous cycle for a second and third time. He observes on each occasion a rising tide of excitation. Then, gradually increasing the tempo to a rapid movement, he proceeds with the in-and-out rhythm until his partner experiences her first orgasm.

Since little more than a minute has transpired during this new undertaking, his own climax is well under control. Consequently, simultaneous orgasms can be experienced at the time of any of his wife's subsequent climaxes.

Following his partner's first orgasm, the husband should pause from 30 seconds to a minute before attempting to induce a second. Then, he proceeds immediately with a deep, brisk, forward and backward rhythm. The second orgasm will occur within 15 seconds and will be shorter and less intense. Thereafter, subsequent climaxes are to be brought about in the same manner and will be found to reduce themselves in strength until the maximum is reached.

The first orgasm is always the longest and strongest, varying in time from 45 seconds to 1½ minutes. Those following rarely extend beyond 15 seconds, and the pauses taken in between by the husband, become relatively longer with each climax.

As a previous chapter has explained, it is unnecessary to utilize the "rise and fall" foreplay with a multi-orgasm woman, although it is not forbidden. It is a matter of choice. But with a wife capable of only one climax, it should not be neglected. However, if a husband of the latter wishes to experiment for the purpose of discontinuing digital clitoral contact during the orgasm, he, too, should abandon the "rise and fall" technique and utilize the penis immediately. In the event he fails and must revert to his former procedure, the following modification may be introduced: while inserted, the husband, as usual, engages in digital clitoral stimulation. Upon the customary sudden, convulsive embrace he receives from his wife as her climax begins, he can discontinue clitoral excitation and utilize the rapid in-and-out motion. He may also achieve his own orgasm if he wishes.

At the conclusion, his partner should advise him whether any decrease in sensation occurred when he discontinued clitoral stimulation. If none did, the probability is strong that further conditioning will enable her to respond eventually with a minimum of clitoral excitation.

The question now arises as to why, after years of climaxes dependent upon clitoral stimulation, orgasm suddenly occurs without it. The basic element is the deepening of affection that has been taking place between the marriage partners throughout this prolonged period. As we all know, much of our sexual emotion is based upon mental excitation. As man and woman reach their peak of mutual affection, a wife feels more closely bound to her husband than ever. During the sex act, this feeling is particularly strong and translates itself into mental excitement. This added to the physical stimulation taking place in the genital area by the deep thrust of the penis, has sufficient force to increase the usual sexual emotion beyond its normal pitch. The result is that this additional mental stimulation works sympathetically upon the clitoral area, the area of sexual sensation, and upsets the normal balance of stimulation and resistance. Orgasm results. But it must be emphasized that this transition comes about only when the male and female ultimately realize that their union has been a successful one.

The suggestions laid down herein have practical value. They are specific and constitute definite and precise intercourse techniques. They have taken into consideration the sexual natures of women in general and in particular. And they are well within the capabilities of any normal husband who is interested in performing his sexual duties unselfishly and competently.

9.

The Sexual Reactions of the Male

MUCH has been written about the sexual emotions and habits of the female, but very little, by comparison, about the male. This is not surprising since, from the standpoint of psychology and physical structure, woman is by far the more interesting and complicated of the sexes. Man, on the other hand, is a relatively simple sexual machine, running on a single track and headed in only one direction. All men could easily have been stamped out and assembled on the same production line so far as their sexual emotions propel them, so far as their capabilities exist for satisfying themselves, and so far as their capacities for giving satisfaction extend.

Man sees a woman and immediately desires her. Within one minute he can automatically sustain an erection, within two minutes can experience orgasm, and within three minutes can be sound asleep. That is the skeleton of his sexual individuality. Men vary, of course, but their variations are slight and only such as are to be expected. Consequently, there is little to be said about the sexual behavior of the normal man.

One does not think of erogenous zones in connection with a man, because for all practical purposes he has only two: the mouth and the penis. As with a woman, it is true that any area of the male body in contact with that of a

123

female part will induce desire if the couple is denied privacy. In bed, however, bodily contact localizes itself.

Generally speaking, a man is stimulated by a woman's mouth anywhere, but by her hand only at the genitals. Specifically, the neck, mouth, breast nipples, waist, groin, genitals, and inside thigh are responsive only to oral contact. The ear and shoulder are not to be considered. Practically speaking, unless a woman goes out of her way to stimulate her husband, which few unfortunately do, the only erogenous zones brought into play are the mouth and genitals. Man is the exploratory creature, and the preponderance of his pre-intercourse excitement comes from handling the female.

The entire male sex is, as a rule, easily and readily aroused. Although preferring to spend a few minutes in exploring the female body, any man can successfully engage in intercourse after a minute of intimate contact with his partner. Orgasm can be attained easily within two minutes, and is usually not sustained longer than three-quarters of a minute. A man experiences no more than one true orgasm during a relationship; should he sustain more, it is only because the first was incomplete. Such an occurrence will take place not more than once in a hundred acts of intercourse. In fact, it is doubtful that the average man will experience three double orgasms in an entire lifetime.

Abatement is almost immediate; within a minute or less, he is thoroughly cooled. Although he may occasionally feel exhausted following orgasm and lie completely limp and relaxed, this is not a state of emotion. It is a state of recuperation. Once the fever of the male has subsided, further sexual intimacy for the period is disagreeable. He loses with absolute completeness all sexual desire for the woman at his side. Even his kisses are an effort and a

FRONTAL SECTION OF MALE GENITALIA

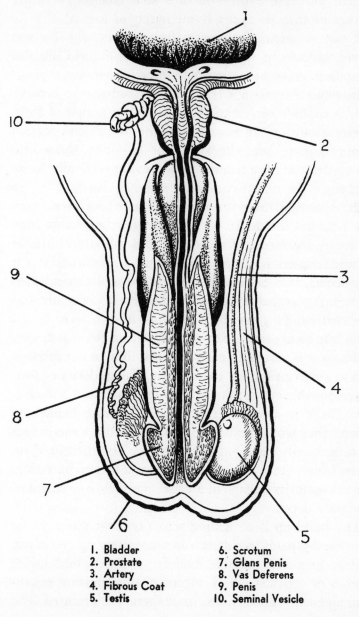

1. Bladder	6. Scrotum
2. Prostate	7. Glans Penis
3. Artery	8. Vas Deferens
4. Fibrous Coat	9. Penis
5. Testis	10. Seminal Vesicle

forced, insincere expression of sexual feeling. Anything further he may do is the result purely of a sense of duty and not emotion. Frequently he wonders why he was cursed with desire, since it is such a relief to feel calm and composed. Now, he wishes only to be left alone.

In connection with a repeated intercourse, the average man is capable of restimulation within a period of from fifteen minutes to an hour. Sometimes the second orgasm is more intense; sometimes it is not. However, the second can be delayed for a lengthy period with practically no effort, since the initial emotional stage obviously is not so high. Although there are occasions on which every man has indulged the desire for a repeated relationship, such occasions are rare and are deleterious to male health. It is more frequent for a woman to desire a repetition. When this occurs, it is because she was not completely satisfied in the first place, although it does happen occasionally that repeated intimacy may be wanted for its own sake.

As is to be expected, passion is a varying element among males, as it is among females, but it is limited to eagerness and to behavior during the orgasm. The majority of men are reasonably gentle; the rhythm they maintain is moderate. There is a large group, however, who behave as though they would tear a woman apart, and some in fact do occasionally cause vaginal bleeding. The rhythm, then, varies from a slow, deep penetration to a furious battering, but the majority engage in a brisk, energetic movement of moderate depth.

The build-up is a tickling sensation that starts in the head of the penis, seems to run completely up the organ as it gathers a pleasurable intensity, and then bursts with a series of convulsive and uncontrollable spurting expansions and contractions as the male sperm is ejaculated. The male exhibits a tendency to accelerate the tempo of his rhythm as a climax approaches in an endeavor to bring it on with a rush. As soon as the spurting has ceased, the male has the desire to relax, and it is this reaction, if he succumbs to it, which leaves his partner unsatisfied.

One fact should be emphasized. Once climax has been attained, if it is of the individual orgasm type, such as it is with the male, passion abates rapidly for both men and women. There is one difference, however. Whereas the male now prefers to forget the relationship as quickly as possible, a woman is not averse to and, indeed, prefers, a measure of petting as if to be assured that her husband's affection for her is just as deep as it appeared to be some minutes previously. The thoughtful male, then, will drop off to sleep with his arms about his wife and will continue to hold her close until such time as she is inclined to fall asleep. That is the proper finale. Every woman resents deeply the brusque tendency of the male to say "Good Night" wearily and turn over on his side. All the physical attraction created during the preceding interval is immediately cancelled by such indifference. A woman may never complain about this. She may complain about the roughness of his beard, and even this she will do timidly and apologetically, but rarely about his sexual oversights. Certain behaviors the male himself must remember, because a woman will hesitate to mention them.

Perhaps the greatest variation among men is their behavior during the orgasm. Like women, some burst into sobbing, others shake their head violently and utter cries which may be heard in adjoining rooms, others whimper softly. These are the highly passionate type and represent the minority. The remainder react generally the same. Some may pant more violently than others, but usually, the orgasm results in a deep breathing as if the male had totally exhausted himself, which for the moment he has.

If a male is breathing heavily during the build-up, it is sometimes difficult for a woman to determine when he has reached the climax. Of course, she never has any trouble detecting the orgasm of the highly passionate, but with one who is more reserved in his behavior, particularly if contraceptive devices are being used or if the vagina is not sensitive, it is almost impossible to determine the orgastic point.

Man's sexual ignorance is largely the cause of the incompatibility so prominent today. However, his chief error is one of omission rather than commission, and since faults of the former are usually the lesser of the two evils, they are the more easily corrected. Compared sexually with woman, nature has smiled upon him. He is quickly aroused and certain to be satisfied, but woman has been constructed as a complete opposite. Indeed, two natures could hardly be less compatible than the sexual natures of man and woman. Therefore, it is not remarkable that sexual incompatibility exists as a constant threat, since nature seems purposefully to have done all she can to encourage it. How important to matrimonial permanence, then, is the need for proper sexual adjustment!

10.

Positions in Intercourse

I N the discussion of physical relationships, it may be well
to include some comment on the desirability, the advantage, and the practicability of various positions assum-
able in sexual intercourse. It is realized there has been considerable hearsay with respect to this matter; that the
average man has encountered much, suggesting the existence of numerous and interesting possibilities in position
additional to those with which everyone is familiar.

This is loose talk and is not to be taken seriously, regardless of hearsay. There are only six basic positions, all conventional, and any others must be considered inconsequential variations thereof.

Although all the basic positions are by no means desirable, necessity frequently forces a couple to adopt one of
them. Various names are applied to them, but for the sake
of simplicity, the word or phrase most descriptive will be
employed. Set down in no particular order, these are the
"man-above position," the "man-below position," the
"side position," the "rear-entry position," the standing position," and the 'sitting position." The variations which
any of these may take are obvious, and it is unnecessary
to set them all down, particularly since the variations are
not so effective as the basic positions themselves.

As simple examples, the man-below position may be
combined with the rear-entry position. However, the con-

ventional manner of assuming the rear-entry position—with the female on her hands and knees, the male on his knees, clasping her about the body—is preferable since this would give him the opportunity not only of fondling the breasts but also of giving digital stimulation to the clitoris. Similarly, the sitting position may be combined with the rear-entry position, but since in the conventional manner the couple face each other, the woman astride the man, this would normally be the choice. The male can simultaneously kiss his partner's breasts and allow her to lean forward for closer genital contact, possibly even allowing the penis and clitoris to meet occasionally.

Considering the positions by themselves aside from any particular preference, since this is wholly a matter of individual choice, the one allowing the greatest intimacy is the side position. Properly assumed, the male is lying on the left side, the female on her right with her right leg between both of her partner's and her left, thrust upward, knee bent, and lying across his right hip. No other position allows the crotches of the couple such intimate contact. At the same time, it is possible for the male to kiss either the female mouth or her breasts by the slightest shift of position. However, for a couple who prefer rapid rhythm, this would hardly be the selection. It is the position for people who prefer slow and deep contact.

The man-above position is probably the one engaged in by the majority. There is nothing at all imaginative about it, but it does permit the fastest rhythm. While some authorities are inclined to be critical if the male fails to rest most of his weight on his elbows, it may be said that this indicates a rather limited experience, since many women desire to have the male wrap his arms about them, pressing their breasts against his and engaging in passionate kissing. The rule always to be kept in mind is to behave in whatever manner the woman prefers.

In the man-above position, it may be necessary for a woman to clasp her legs about the male waist or raise them, knees bent, above the waist, to allow him easier or deeper access. Adjustment may be made also by placing a pillow under the female buttocks to elevate the vagina to a suitable height. These adjustments are independent of the size of the female; it is as necessary on occasion to adjust for a tall woman as for a short one.

The chief advantage of the man-below position lies in the fact that it enables a woman to take the initiative and satisfy herself completely while imposing the least amount of activity and consequent restraint upon the male.

The rear-entry position is probably seldom employed. When large abdomens are involved, it is the most satisfactory, particularly when combined with the sitting position. Although it allows the male the use of his hands, there is less warmth to intimacy involving abdomen against buttocks than abdomen against abdomen.

The sitting position, most frequently used as a matter of expediency, necessity, or as a break in the monotony of the usual bedroom routine, can be reversed effectively by having the woman instead of the man sit on a fairly low object such as a divan or arm chair. Leaning back and throwing her legs over the shoulders of the male, who is resting on his knees, she enables a deep and close contact to be effected.

The standing position, in which for greater comfort the female should stand on some elevation to avoid the necessity of having the male bend his knees, is definitely an emergency measure. Young people, secretly wed and living with their respective parents, or couples who live apart and have no privacy, are usually driven to this extreme. This position is an alternative of desperation and permits no great degree of comfort whatever.

It must be emphasized, regardless of the position described, that no two couples will or can assume it in the identical manner. For that reason it is not possible to advise exactly how far forward or backward, for example, a man should be situated in assuming the man-above position. Individuals will always find it necessary to make some minor adjustment to conform with their preferences, physical differences, or comfort. Nor can the same position necessarily be assumed identically with two women of approximate size and proportion. Slightly slimmer thighs, while making little apparent difference in the physical appearance of two women, can make a surprising difference with respect to the adjustment necessary in copulation. Likewise, the slant of the pelvic bone or the amount of flesh covering it may completely alter the possibility of the male organ engaging the clitoris, an accomplishment supremely difficult, if not out of the question at any time. Even the position of the clitoris itself, or the location, angle, or size of the vaginal canal varies from woman to woman. Obviously, fleshy buttocks will elevate a female higher and appear to offer readier access to the vagina than will slimness of build in the same area. On the other hand, this seeming advantage may be offset by a more acute slant of the vaginal canal, or a compensating obliqeness of canal structure on the part of a thin woman.

Consequently, a position, comfortable and enjoyable with one woman, can be entirely out of the question with another; and, of course, practically the same comments can be made with respect to a man. It is important, then, that every couple experiment with the customary basic positions and make minor adjustments thereto in order to discover the ones in which they are the most relaxed. Relaxation is essential to a perfect sex relationship. While it is foolish to go out of one's way to devise some far-fetched posture, it is always intelligent to effect improvement wherever possible.

In closing this chapter, it should be remarked that proper and perfect sexual intercourse is a matter of good technique combined with a certain limited knowledge of biology and anatomy, with emphasis on the former. With good technique, any normal woman can be satisfied. Without it, failure is the almost inevitable consequence.

11.

The Sex Act Systematized

THE foregoing chapters contain a wide variety of information concerned with the sexual association of man and woman. From these sections it has been thought expedient to extract the facts pertinent exclusively to conducting the sexual relationship, emphasize them, set them down in the form of a procedure, and add some comments which have been reserved for such a summary.

A man who has given study to the previous material should be able now to approximate the emotional level of any woman during the first relationship. The level of a wife with whom he has been living over a long period should present practically no problem at all. Nor should any woman who has read the sections be doubtful of her position in the emotional scale of sex; she and her husband should know precisely how she should be treated.

Of course, the single woman who has preserved her chastity is unaware of her sexual potentialities. If she assumes them, she may be entirely wrong. The romantic girl, the type subject to heavy crushes, is as often on a lower level as on a higher; her pre-marital emotion is not necessarily an index to her sexual responsiveness.

Regarding intercourse specifically, proper procedure suggests that a man observe certain cardinal rules. The first of these is to approach every woman as if she were on a low level and slow to arouse. This will entail embracing all the elements of foreplay as described in the appropriate chapter.

The second rule demands that a man devote no less than fifteen minutes or longer to foreplay unless otherwise directed by the female.

With respect to intercourse itself, the most comfortable or practical position is assumed. If it is intended that the female have unrestrained freedom, for example, then the man-below position is the most suitable. This position has also the quality at times of increasing the emotion of any woman.

Careful clitoral stimulation should precede the first female orgasm and the rise-and-fall technique should be applied for at least a series of six. The third rule, then, requires the observance of digital stimulation of the clitoris both prior to and during the orgasm unless the female is of the highly passionate type; clitoral contact need then be observed only during foreplay.

Since one cannot predetermine the number of orgasms of which a woman is capable, the male should delay his climax until his partner cannot experience another or unless she is approaching the end of her cycle; following this he must be prepared to continue digital stimulation until his partner no longer responds. This may be regarded as the fourth rule and pertains to the individual-orgasm type.

Irrespective of type, if the male cannot delay his orgasm with the penis in motion or cannot continue the motion following his climax, he engages in digital clitoral stimulation or digital vaginal stimulation until his partner is satisfied. This may be done with the penis inserted but inactive, and constitutes the fifth rule.

No man can predict with certainty the appropriate moment to engage in the simultaneous orgasm. Consequently the sixth rule suggests that a man apply himself to extending the female climax and ignore the features of the simultaneous orgasm unless the female requests it.

Male abatement is rapid and thorough, following climax; the female abatement is not. The seventh and last rule insists that the husband display some measure of post-intercourse affection.

No emotionally aroused woman ever kisses with her eyes open or keeps them open to any extent during intimacy. A woman with open eyes is still cold. However, an adequate male lover never closes his eyes when actively engaged. He is alert to determine the responses of his partner and closed eyes encourage dreaminess. This prerogative belongs exclusively to a woman.

It is well to emphasize that the female body is not an instrument existing solely to satisfy the passion of the male, although many careless husbands appear to think otherwise. Actually, the male body should exist for a woman's pleasure, and a man with the proper attitude will derive added enjoyment from the emotion of his wife. There is such a thing as "bedroom manners," and it may be well to devote a few paragraphs to them.

An experienced lover never makes a conspicuous approach to a sex relationship. He regards it as a perfectly natural urge and restrains himself from any behavior which overemphasizes his mood. A refined woman expects a man to control his passion, and she repudiates any crude overtures to sex indulgence. Even in the privacy of her home or bedroom, a woman feels entitled to demand sexual dignity on the part of her husband.

Actually, an aroused woman is no less responsive to the sex urge than man, and in many cases is more so. This, however, has not been given the same prominence as that devoted to depicting man as crude and animalistic in his passion. So, like Caesar's wife, he must hold himself well above suspicion, or run the risk of developing in his mate an aversion founded upon his lack of sexual polish.

Although a man may feel the greatest mental tenderness and affection toward his wife, he feels at the same time a normal body hunger, entirely divorced from the other. Nevertheless, he avoids gloating over her nude body as she is disrobing or giving the impression that her nudity alone has the capability of stimulating desire. Such behavior can add to the self-consciousness, reserve, and over-developed modesty which many woman never lose, although married to a man for a lifetime. Such women are usually the lowly or moderately passionate, and present a sufficient problem to their husbands.

Finally, no self-respecting or intelligent male will badger his wife or urge intimacy upon her if she, for any reason whatever, is disinclined. It is difficult to see how a forced relationship can be a pleasurable experience for a man when he knows that his mood is not reciprocated. The enjoyment of his wife's passion should occupy the foremost position in his mind; and a vital element to a satisfactory relationship is lacking when a woman merely performs in a mechanical fashion. A man who will insist upon his rights as a husband regardless of his wife's rights as a human being is thoroughly deserving of the general reputation the male sex unfortunately bears, and is one of those responsible for it.

The old platitude, "Familiarity breeds contempt," is so true and so well-phrased that, if for nothing else, it should be venerated for its antiquity. There is no point in saying that a man should always respect his wife, because human nature has decided otherwise, and perhaps everyone occasionally forgets himself. With regard to sexual intimacy, however, there can be no excuse. It is far too personal an involvement ever to allow one's best behavior to be forgotten even for a moment.

12.

Oral Connection

THE practice of oral connection, in which the male and female genitals are stimulated directly by mouth, lip, or tongue rhythms, receives little attention and considerable neglect in printed discussions of human sexual habits. Although this procedure is so widespread as to be elemental in sexual behavior, many inhibit the impulse for one reason or another. Let us consider conceivable objections and give them frank appraisal.

To begin with, the practice is completely normal. When millions engage in it and additional millions suppress the tendency, it can scarcely be regarded otherwise. However, to many minds, any method of behavior which deviates too far from the conventional has the color of depravity.

Of course, few will admit in their everyday conversations that they indulge in the practice, since each participant is inclined to regard himself as an exception. No mother, regardless of her own sex behavior, would think of discussing it with her daughter, nor would a father with his son. Yet in some way both offspring should acquire a clear understanding of the matter. Sooner or later, it may arise, and when it does, it should be regarded with an enlightened and objective attitude, not with shock and narrow concepts. The uninformed bride of a few weeks may suddenly find herself engaged in this experience with her newly-wed husband; so may a naive groom with a highly passionate wife. Neither must allow a germ of ignorance to breed the suspicion that depravity exists.

If the practice of oral connection be analyzed with an open mind, it will be found that the prejudices regarding it have no basis in fact; that a distorted imagination is largely responsible for a negative attitude. The reasons for prejudice are obvious. Firstly, the tendency is unconsciously associated with homosexualism, the thought of which is disagreeable to normal people. The mere fact that two persons of the same sex can react passionately toward each other, is sufficient to condemn their primary means of sexual outlet, even though this identical means of outlet may likewise be employed by completely normal individuals of opposite sexes.

Of course, there is no more justification for this narrow view than for the conclusion that kissing is a perversion simply because unfortunate homosexuals engage in it also. Consequently, oral rhythm as practiced by members of the opposite sex is completely unrelated to perverted abnormality. That it happens to be a method of homosexual expression is coincidental; both the perverted and the normal use whatever means are available to them.

Secondly, the genital area of our bodies has always been regarded as of doubtful cleanliness. Again, this concept can be faulty if both male and female observe proper hygienic habits.

Oral contact with the ear is a common procedure, practically routine, in love making. In fact the ear represents a powerful erotic zone. The same can be said also of neck. On a warm humid night both areas are subject to various accumulations of an obvious nature and can scarcely be called clean. Many hours of dancing may have passed between the early shower of the evening and subsequent petting party. Can two sweaty bodies be regarded as wholesome? On the other hand, for married couples, it is a mere matter of minutes from tub to bed, and the fastidious of both sexes will, whenever possible, bathe or shower before amative indulgence, then if only to guard against body odor.

Cleanliness is a vital factor regardless of the type of relationship between sexes. There should be no greater relaxation in its application to one part of the body than to another. If anything, greater caution should be exercised in any area likely to offend. Among the civilized, specific attention is given the genital region.

The kiss is a sexual element the abandonment of which no reasonable person would recommend. However, it cannot be defended on any hygienic principle. The mouth and throat are constant incubators of disease, with salivary pools of dangerous and even deadly bacteria floating within. This does not include the less harmful, though actually more revolting accumulations of mucous resulting from an inflamed sinus, congested lungs, a simple head cold, or the decayed food particles lodged between the teeth or in some hidden cavity. Yet, the same people who pretend shock and disgust at the thought of oral connection, will readily and indiscriminatly engage in the "soul kiss." They will unhesitatingly probe their partner's mouth with, perhaps, a coated tongue, and encourage a similar response in return.

This is, of course, a most disgusting description of the most common method of sexual expression. But no one can deny its faithfulness or justify it on any grounds of cleanliness. The plain, bare-faced fact emerges that the delightful kiss is a thoroughly unsanitary convention.

Notwithstanding, it and its inevitable salivary exchange are almost universally accepted, and must be as long as people are impelled by the sex urge, for the kiss actually has a very definite and vital place in the operation of sex.

Common sense suggests that a well-cleansed male organ is free of all odor. A corresponding condition likewise exists where a careful woman is concerned. The tip of the clitoris lies on the surface of the vulva, is an even-textured membrane, is easily reached, and is capable of a more rapid and thorough cleansing than deposits between one's teeth. Both of these genital zones would be more likely to suffer contamination by oral contact than to inflict it. The truth is that the universal kiss is not so wholesome a convention that oral contact with a cleansed genital area need be regarded as a perverted activity. Consequently, where oral connection is concerned, an imaginative rather than actual condition has created the prejudices that exist against it.

Of course, this form of sex play is never engaged in as a day-after-day practice. It severely taxes the nervous system, particularly the male's. The highly passionate woman, however, almost without exception will usually devote some period of foreplay to an oral caressing of the male organ. Generally, mutual activity is reserved for times of superpassion when the emotion of either male or female or both, impels them to find a release requiring the closest and most intimate form of expression. Resulting orgasms are equally as strong and even on occasion stronger when oral attention is given to the female clitoris. The orgastic response of the male to oral contact is, as a rule, greater.

In continental Europe this practice is as common as intercourse, and the hygienic habits of the European woman tend to encourage it. For example, in most countries

—France, Holland, Germany, Austria, Czechoslovakia—to mention only a few, the homes of the upper class, as well as many of the middle class, contain in the bathroom, besides the toilet, another fixture known as the *bidet,* used for the douche.

The bidet has the general shape of a toilet. It is designed in the center, however, to extend toward the vagina in a snout, and eject a strong fountain of water upon the genital area of the female. A faucet on either side, for hot and cold water, controls the temperature and pressure.

The bidet, of course, is a highly civilized feature and should be an essential appurtenance in every American household. It encourages daily douching, a practice not engaged in nearly enough by American women, who usually resort to it only following a sexual relationship or the end of a period. This is not sufficiently frequent to eliminate the secretion formed in the vagina and vaginal vault. Douching should be performed regularly as a matter of routine hygiene.

On the continent of Europe oral connection is as common as intercourse, and sex being what it is, there is no reason to assume differently for other localities. It has been so widely adopted in this country that no one need feel individualistic in its practice.

13.

Controlling the Male Orgasm

WHILE the stress in these chapters has been laid largely upon women's sexual problems, because they are definitely the greater, this section will be devoted to the male's only actual problem, that of self-control. It should at the same time make interesting reading for a woman; serve to make her understand why she is frequently unsatisfied in sex relationships, and perhaps enable her to take a more tolerant attitude where she is absolutely certain her husband is doing his best. What this represents has been described in another chapter, and a woman should never be satisfied with less.

It has been stated that woman's sexual problems are greater than man's from both points of view because each is concerned with them. She is concerned with seeing that she is satisfied, and he with seeing that he satisfies her. His satisfaction presents no difficulty. It may be possible for him to experience more enjoyment when his wife releases her inhibitions, but he will in any event be satisfied so long as she allows intimacy.

This is, however, not true for a normal woman. Too many conditions, elsewhere discussed, may interfere with her ultimate satisfaction, but nothing can interfere with the eventual satisfaction of the normal man. So long as he attains orgasm he is satisfied, and every normal man can attain it regardless of the conditions surrounding the intimacy.

He will experience orgasm whether or not he wears a condom, whether or not he practices coitus interruptus—withdrawal before orgasm and a most unsatisfactory method for more reasons than one—whether or not his wife uses an inserted contraceptive, whether or not the female hand is the medium, whether or not external genital contact induces climax, whether or not it be premature. In short, regardless of the conditions, any normal man will experience orgasm and consequent satisfaction. This is not necessarily true of a woman.

It may be well to define satisfaction in practical terms. Satisfaction is attained when orgasm has occurred and the individual man or woman has no immediate further desire for sexual intimacy. The male orgasm almost instantly produces that condition in any normal man. Not only does it almost immediately bring about complete satisfaction, but further dalliance in most cases becomes disagreeable. Unhappily, nature has constructed man in this fashion; he has absolutely no control over the feeling.

Thus, man has been created with three unfortunate weaknesses. He is quick to be aroused, he is speedily satisfied, and he loses the mood and inclination for further sex play almost immediately thereafter. It seems that nature has deliberately conspired against the sexual pleasure of woman; if both sexes had only one of the three differences in common, satisfactory intercourse would present less of a problem.

If man were as slow to arouse as are most women, relatively speaking, both would in all probability be ready for orgasm at approximately the same time, and a closer mutual satisfaction would result. But this is not the case, because man is normally ready for the climax long before his partner.

On the other hand, if man, quickly aroused as he is, required a prolonged excitation before reaching the climax, the female, although slow to become aroused, could overtake him eventually and be ready for orgasm at a time more in keeping with his. But, again, this is not the situation. Once the male is aroused, orgasm is speedily attained and just as speedily spent. The female cannot overtake him.

Alternatively, if following orgasm the male required a certain cooling period and his ardor abated slowly, he would still be in the mood to continue intimacy with his tardy partner despite the fact that he had already achieved his climax. Not only does the mood rapidly disappear; worse still, it is replaced by a distaste for prolonggation, a distaste over which he has absolutely no control. Nature does not even allow him a neutral reaction, and he cannot with vigor and enthusiasm draw out the act too long once he has experienced orgasm. He wishes to be left alone.

Since nature has deliberately created complications, a way must be found to circumvent her, if possible. The only answer is to be found in man's ability to exercise some measure of type of self-control. He must do so if he is to insure his partner's satisfaction. The words "measure" and "type" have been used because self-control can be exercised by the degree of restaint, partial or complete, employed in controlling orgasm, or it can be exerted after the orgasm has occurred by forcing oneself to continue sex play even though futher intimacy has become distasteful. Let us here examine the various types of self-control.

It is the habit of too many men to neglect the important

and vital matter of foreplay almost entirely, engage in intimacy at once, and precipitate their own orgasm as rapidly as possible, either assuming or hoping that their partners will successfully pace them, or not caring whether they do so. These man make no attempt to exert self-control. There are an equal number who engage in foreplay so long as it suits them, whereupon they make connection and effect orgasm at their convenience. This group also ignores self-control.

There is another and smaller group which, although desiring orgasm, will extend the preliminaries to the last notch of their endurance, then make connection, whereupon orgasm occurs almost at once, whether or not their partners have completely sustained their climaxes. These men have partial self-control. There is still another and by far the smallest group who restrain their climaxes until the woman experiences hers in advance or simultaneously. This represents complete self-control. Also falling under this last classification are those men who, despite having attained orgasm prior to their partners, will nevertheless continue intimacy either by hand or penis, regardless of their discomfort, until the woman is completely satisfied.

Falling within these five groups are others whose behavior may vary, such as the man who may carry his restraint past the preliminaries and partially through the intercourse, but who is not quite able to maintain it to a point of female orgasm. Such a man possesses only partial self-control. Then there is the husband who, although almost completely neglecting foreplay, nevertheless does have the staying power to maintain an intimacy until his wife is satisfied. However, any variation will fall quite clearly into one of the five divisions, since these groups include the various degrees of restraint.

There are, however, two methods of insuring complete satisfaction for a woman and which are wholly free from any undesirable elements. They may be described as involving automatic control rather than self-control. These will result in the truest form of perfect intercourse, and should be among the first experiments made by the man who experiences so-called premature orgasm if he wishes to improve his technique. This will be further explained and enlarged upon.

It may be well to discuss at this point the relationship of so-called premature ejaculation to masturbation. First: every man is subject at times to premature ejaculation and often to the general tendency. Nature intended he should be. Second: normal premature ejaculation has no connection with masturbation. By this it is not meant that *excessive* masturbation may not have a bearing on an abnormal ejaculatory condition. The writer means only that the tendency to so-called premature ejaculation possessed by the normal average male has no relationship whatever to the normal masturbation he practiced as a boy.

To begin with, since almost every man has practiced the habit in his youth, and even subsequently, in more or less the same degree, the result should be that no one is capable of exerting self-control. However, many can; in fact, most men can if they make a serious attempt. Furthermore, the only difference between masturbation and sexual intercourse is the fact that sex magnetism and an imponderable psychic element are lacking. Even their presence in intercourse, however, does not relieve the purely physical stress on the various organs involved in the sex act. They only add to the enjoyment. It is perfectly possible to produce orgasm in masturbation with less physical effort than in intercourse, by merely massaging the underside of the head of the penis. Consequently, in the case of the average man, the relationship of youthful masturbation to early orgasm in intercourse is difficult to evaluate.

On the other hand, it is interesting to observe how the relationship of masturbation to orgasm is argued in reverse with respect to woman. There exists a considerable body of statistics purporting to indicate that the majority of women have also indulged in adolescent and adult masturbation. It is contended in the case of the female that this practice has slowed down, not speeded up, her orgastic impulses.

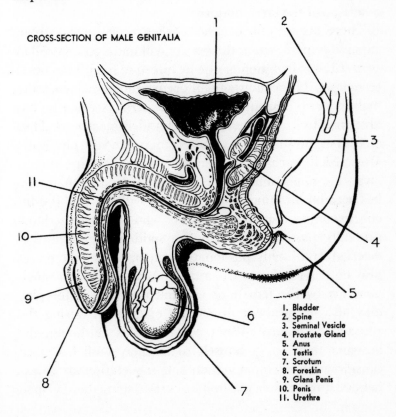

CROSS-SECTION OF MALE GENITALIA

1. Bladder
2. Spine
3. Seminal Vesicle
4. Prostate Gland
5. Anus
6. Testis
7. Scrotum
8. Foreskin
9. Glans Penis
10. Penis
11. Urethra

The theory is advanced that women who experience sex sensation not at the vagina but only at the clitoris can lay this defect to having engaged in clitoral masturbation. This form of indulgence, it is argued, has focused all sensation upon the clitoris with the result that women who have so engaged can experience little or no feeling to a point of impotence. Therefore, we are faced with the question, does masturbation hasten the orgastic process or retard it? It is more reasonable to assume that it does nothing, and to regard these male and female tendencies as completely normal conditions inasmuch as they are characteristic of the large majority.

There are certain occasions when every normal man capable of performing the sex act will undergo a so-called premature ejaculation or else be forced to modify his usual technique. This condition will occur at intervals when the male is more than usually aroused, perhaps when he has abstained from intercourse for a considerable period. This, of course, presumes that the partners are still physically attracted to each other. A man who for the first time is given the opportunity to be intimate with a woman who has been on his mind in a sexual way will also find it difficult to control himself. A widower who has been used to a generally passive wife and who suddenly finds himself married to a highly passionate woman, will at the outset also be carried far ahead of his usual pace. Too much handling by the female or too much activity in foreplay may also bring about premature ejaculation during the ensuing intercourse. What occurs is this: although the husband may apply himself to foreplay with his usual consideration, his imagination and expectation are so expanded during these preliminaries that, immediately upon inserting the male organ, the interior rhythm or contact alone will bring him to a climax almost at once.

Consequently, unless he wishes to complete the orgasm, he must either withdraw or temporarily cease activity until he quiets. More frequently than not, despite this forced inactivity, the ejaculation will proceed spontaneously. This is purely a matter of becoming extraordinarily aroused, perhaps mentally more than physically, and women are just as subject to such occurrences as men. Childhood masturbation does not enter into it.

There are other frequent occasions when a man becomes more than usually aroused for no explainable reason. At such times also, the male must depart from his usual procedure if he is to avoid the so-called premature orgasm. Obviously, self-control is not invariably attainable, and all men will be premature on occasion.

The fact is that the expression "premature orgasm" in its usual application is a misnomer. It is used critically to describe any male orgasm occurring before the female orgasm, and gives an impression of abnormality. Even though some authorities do make a distinction between an orgasm occurring either during foreplay or immediately upon insertion, and one occurring later but prior to the female orgasm, sometimes the distinction is not clarified. The impression remains that most men are victims of abnormal premature orgasm.

This is not at all true. The man who is the victim of actual premature orgasm is an exception and requires some form of treatment. True premature orgasm involves exclusively the constant habit of the male to ejaculate during foreplay or immediately upon insertion of his organ into the vagina. This and this alone is abnormal.

Under ordinary circumstances and in the process of normal intercourse, the male orgasm will always precede the female orgasm unless controlled. Since this is natural, it is hardly premature, and those who control it are actually behaving more unnaturally than those who do not. This is one situation in which nature must be defeated if man is to succeed in satisfying his partner.

Most men, once they have inserted the penis, will experience an orgasm, generally within two minutes, if they create a ceaseless, rhythmic motion. Their partners, unless previously conditioned by foreplay, will not usually react so quickly. There is nothing premature about this orgasm. It is early only with respect to the time of the female, and occurs within the time intended by nature.

There are times, also, when overexcitement in foreplay causes orgasm before insertion. This is not premature. A man can withstand just so much excitement, no matter how it is induced, before he gives way to orgasm. On the other hand, if a man continually achieves orgasm during only moderate foreplay, such orgasms are strictly premature, since they occur too frequently outside the boundaries of the average man's experience.

The question, then, is how to go about developing self-control. It should be emphasized that every normal man who engages in intercourse regularly can, except on occasions of unusual excitement, postpone the moment of orgasm until the proper time, the proper time being whenever he cares to have it, provided he can insure the fact that he will not leave his partner unsatisfied. This question of time is complicated by his partner's variable nature. She may be slowly aroused and slowly satisfied. She may be slow to arouse but quick to be satisfied. She may be quickly aroused and slowly satisfied. Finally, she may be quickly aroused and quickly satisfied. While it depends entirely upon the individual nature of the woman, usually no such individuality exists with respect to man.

When we realize that many men requiring only two or three minutes for sexual satisfaction are wed to women who may require thirty minutes, the nature of the problem becomes clear. We must, therefore, consider the elements which contribute to producing orgasm in the male and retard them until the time of proper release. There are only four principal ones: thought, sight, contact, and motion. Hearing and smell may also play a part, but it is too slight to be discussed.

Though the lover does not realize it, much of his sexual stimulation springs from the brain. Desire is only translated thought. All men know that an erection can be created simply by imagining an intimate situation with a woman. In actual intercourse, the brain is also at work, enabling man to experience the pleasure which comes from handling a woman's body or from realizing the extent of her emotion. Consequently, the brain must be harnessed, because it is the greatest stimulant when concentrated on man's own enjoyment, which primarily is where it does not belong.

In this connection, a word may be said regarding a form of sexual relationship known as the Karezza, a form of indulgence which may be described as immobile intercourse. Once coupled, the partners relax and revel in a pure state of mental ectasy, maintaining no rhythm and attaining no orgasm. Those who can condition themselves to this type of relationship can be said to have achieved the unique ultimate in sexual sensation. All the most desirable elements are present; a lazy and lengthy state of delight; complete satisfaction for both partners; and a minimum of exertion. However, as much as the author believes in the power of mental enjoyment and advocates its development to the fullest degree, he doubts that any sensation was intended by nature to exceed that of the orgasm. It is unlikely that nature, whose primary object is the perpetuation of the race, would allow the existence of a sensation superior to the climax and one which would defeat her purposes.

Sight, naturally, will stimulate desire if the intimacy is conducted in the light. But in the dark, where most relationships take place, it loses importance.

Contact definitely increases passion. The female hand stroking or squeezing the penis can bring about orgasm. The male hand exploring the female body, as well as the mutual contact of genitals, will increase stimulation. Kissing contributes to the excitement, particularly if the woman has an eager mouth and an active tongue.

Lastly, the motion of rhythmic movement, once the penis has been inserted, will speedily bring about orgasm.

These, then, are the elements which contribute toward producing orgasm in the male. He must establish control over all of them.

What is said next may sound strange, but nevertheless, must be accepted if benefit is to result. It is not possible for a man to devote himself dutifully to satisfying his wife without sacrificing a measure of sexual convenience. However, to the same extent that he sacrifices his, he also increases hers. But—and all men are urged to regard this point seriously, because it represents the soul of perfect sexual compatibility—the mental satisfaction which results from realizing that one's partner is being gratified in a manner no other man can surpass, will transform itself in time to a feeling of pleasure which will far exceed the small measure of sexual convenience of which the male has deprived himself.

A man will grow to enjoy the gratification he is producing in his partner far more than any other emotion experienced in a relationship, outside of the orgasm, and it will leave him thoroughly satisfied and content. In doing this, he can bind his wife to him tighter than all the marriage vows can, because she will realize that there exists no other man with a greater capacity for giving her sexual comfort, and she will feel no urge to look elsewhere. In other words, in denying himself a certain amount of physical convenience, a man more than makes up for it in the mental enjoyment he acquires and which transforms itself into pure sexual pleasure.

Having said that man must sacrifice some of his sexual convenience, let us consider it. A woman can be thoroughly gratified only when she abandons herself completely to the pleasures of a relationship and is allowed to do so. Should a man indulge the identical tendency, his abandonment is short-lived and the relationship is speedily terminated. Therefore, he dare not do so. Since nature has created him with this desire, any restraint he imposes upon himself naturally reduces his pleasure. How is he to contain himself without destroying his enjoyment?

Let us start with the control of thought. If a man concentrates thoroughly upon his procedure for successfully arousing his wife and estimates the extent of her passion from time to time, he will discover that he cannot do this and simultaneously keep his mind exclusively upon the pleasure he alone is extracting from intimacy. He will feel only an indirect enjoyment from his own excitement, since no one can fully concentrate upon two things at the same time. He will discover also that he will enjoy his wife's reactions and that they will become more important to his pleasure than his own physical excitement, which can easily be heightened at will. Since this constant watching for his wife's reaction is a mental process, the physical is retarded, and he will observe that she constantly rises to a higher pitch while he can maintain a fairly consistent level.

It is not possible, however, for a man to avoid momentarily abandoning himself to the voluptuous enjoyment which follows when he first clasps his nude partner and their bodies seek each other in intimate embrace. He will find, nevertheless, that a minute of this unrestrained pleasure produces quite a release of tension and expectation, and that he can then turn his attention to the important matter of arousing his partner. He will observe, too, that his own excitement will mount more gradually with his partner's, following hers, instead of leading.

Regarding sight, little control is required. If the intimacy takes place in the dark, it is an unimportant element. Even in the light, its effect is no more than an initial and passing source of excitement. The lover may run his eyes for a few moments over the desirable features of his partner, but eye appetite is quickly satisfied, and the pleasure that ensues from the mingling of the bodies at once crowds eye appeal to the background.

Contact is the second factor most important in preventing the delay of orgasm. Thought is subtle and nebulous, but contact is aggressive and immediate. The real danger lies in the fact that too much motion on the part of the male at the outset of foreplay will arouse him to a condition of intense excitement at a time when that of his partner is just beginning to develop. Since foreplay requires initially a relaxed, searching, and watchful attitude by the male, an excess of bodily exertion at the outset must be minimized. Moreover, although it gives him pleasure to have his partner fondle his genitals and although it may also be pleasurable to the partner, he must limit it and put a complete stop to it as soon as he begins to feel involuntary spasms in the penis and no later than the first dull suggestion of tingling, which is the forerunner of speedy orgasm. However, if he devotes his exclusive attention toward arousing his partner, it is possible for the female to fondle the male organ extensively without creating the risk of early climax.

Oddly, the average woman is awkward in handling the male genitals, and frequently lacks the capacity to produce orgasm in that manner, except after much effort which tires her, bores her, and irritates the male. She seems to lack an instinctive conception of the proper technique, and remains a slow pupil even when instructed. Any man, regardless of his immaturity, easily excels her in the delicate matter of arousing excitement. Her mouth is her chief asset. The wife who would be effective in deliberately arousing her husband must learn to use her hands with a certain amount of understanding. This is important, since a woman who is in a sexual mood may find it necessary on occasion to stimulate a husband who, while not averse to

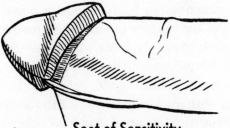

Seat of Sensitivity

relationship, may at the time be indifferent to one. The wife is entitled to make her desires known, and she should do so.

In this connection then, a woman should bear in mind that, however she begins to stimulate the male organ, the same procedure should be unceasingly maintained until it produces the desired result. It should be gentle, because the nerves in the head of the penis are as sensitive as those of the clitoris. Too much pressure upon the clitoris will deaden its sensitivity; it has the same effect on the penis. To use her hand in a satisfactory manner, a woman should be certain that the rhythmic motion includes brushing the underside of the glans with her hand; or she can concentrate upon this section of the head entirely with her finger, rubbing the underside in much the same manner as the male massages the clitoris. The head of the penis, particularly the under portion, is actually the center of male sensation as indicated on the foregoing diagram. The remainder is not too responsive and reacts largely through sympathy. Once sensation becomes strong, she may then grasp the entire organ and apply a rhythmic movement.

Like most men, women also expect immediate reaction from whatever technique they employ. Should the male fail to respond with rapidity, they introduce another approach, returning to the original after a period of unsuccessful experimentation. Each change of procedure causes the emotion of the partner to drop, until finally the matter becomes a wearisome chore for which women lack future enthusiasm. But it is as much their duty to be capable in this respect as it is their husbands'.

A woman with an active mouth can raise havoc with a man's emotions if he allows himself to concentrate on its stimulating quality. But if he makes it his purpose to match her oral ardor, which is an unconscious manifestation of her mounting passion, he will be dwelling on his own performance rather than hers. In this way he will not only increase her emotion but will offset the ability she may have to stimulate him.

His hands are his most important asset. They do the greatest part of the preliminary work and usually prolong the female orgasm. A man with a delicate, caressing touch is a far more adequate lover than one with only a well-developed penis. Although his investigation of the female body is capable of inducing erection in the male it cannot produce orgasm in him unless he is a victim of premature ejaculation in its correct sense. However, it is normal for the inexperienced adolescent or an adult who has infrequent sexual society, or who has never engaged in intercouse, to ejaculate upon merely touching the private zone of a woman, provided some prestimulating activity has already taken place. He has not yet become accustomed to the regular opportunity of fondling the female body, opportunity that accompanies a state of matrimony. To him, touching a female breast or surface genitals, even though covered with clothing, represents one of the ultimates in his sexual experience. It is not surprising that his mind should carry him to orgasm as it does any normal male who has had a voluptuous dream.

These, then, are the types of control involved in contact. We now arrive at intercourse, the only infallible and positive method that will produce a speedy orgasm in every normal male. While this is also a matter of contact, it has been given its own place, because it is by its nature not dependent on any other means of excitation included in sexual relationship and will insure climax with greater rapidity and facility than anything else.

Copulation taxes all men, even those with self-control, to the utmost, because a second of movement too much on the part of either male or female will cause the former to attain orgasm. Furthermore, the tendency is such that, once having started the motion, the male finds the sensation so overpowering that he feels compelled to continue it until climax is achieved.

Supposing, however, that at the moment of insertion, it will take the female three minutes to reach orgasm and that her orgasm or orgasms will endure for another four. Is it possible for the male to stretch his inadequate two minutes into the seven required by his partner? While the answer is a positive one, it cannot be done with full physical pleasure to the male. It cannot be done by relying strictly upon the movement of the penis to bring about satisfaction of his partner during the seven minutes required.

It stands to reason that, if a rhythmic motion of steady or increasing rapidity will produce orgasm in the male in the neighborhood of two minutes, the only way to extend it beyond that time is to reduce the speed. Consequently, the male must cut his rhythm down and frequently stop completely, because the mental excitement of knowing he is closely connected with his partner also adds impetus to the approaching orgasm. Since the sensation is so delightful, he neither wishes to reduce his rhythm nor stop, yet he is forced to do one or the other or both. This opposition to nature's impulse is both difficult and undesirable.

Since his partner's orgasm is completely dependent upon a constant and uninterrupted flow of movement, every interruption also reduces the height of her ecstasy. As a result, she cannot attain orgasm or have her orgasm prolonged unless one partner continuously maintains the rhythm; if this is done, he will experience orgasm before her and perhaps thereafter be unable to extend the intimacy to the point necessary for her satisfaction. The problem is greater where the male requires two minutes and the female perhaps fifteen minutes.

There are only three solutions to this difficulty: the male must stimulate his partner digitally to a point approximating orgasm before he inserts himself, and thereafter depend upon the two minutes and his endurance following his own orgasm to bring his partner complete satisfaction; or, while reducing his rhythm, he must continue to stimulate her digitally so that no interruption occurs, at the same time forcing his mind to dwell on something quite outside the relationship; or he must force himself, following his orgasm, to continue the rhythm either digitally or by the penis. This last can be very difficult for the male.

It will be recalled that this chapter has previously referred to a condition described as "automatic control." When this exists, or has been created—though it is not attainable on occasions when the male is highly excited—the most satisfactory kind of relationship faces the female, with little inconvenience to the male. Once this condition has been achieved, future repetitions of it with the same woman can follow with desirable frequency, and the husband realizes that he has become as proficient in sexual intercourse as is possible. The man who finds it difficult to delay orgasm should start immediately to experiment with this.

As all married men know, there are occasions when sexual intimacy has no particular appeal to them. They are not necessarily tired, nervous, or mentally or physically disturbed. They simply have no sexual desire for their wives at that time.

The fact that man experiences no physical desire at a certain period does not mean that he is incapable of being aroused. A male can be excited at any time whether he be tired or rested, nervous or calm. Kisses or bodily contact may not be effective, but the penis will unfailingly be erected if the female fondles it. Once the penis is rigid, desire will eventually result.

This being the case, there is absolutely no reason why he should deny his wife his sexual society if she desires it. The fact that he lacks the mood does not mean that intimacy will prove unhealthful or ultimately distasteful. If he now encourages it, he will discover that his staying power is immeasurably increased, and with good reason. Since his attitude is one of indifference, the brain fails to build up expectation and sexual excitement. The burden is placed almost entirely upon his physical reaction, and he approximates the condition of a woman slow to arousal. His hands explore the female body, but the movement is largely mechanical and his mind extracts little pleasure from it. Even kissing lacks flavor, and erection develops slowly.

This mood, however, does not transmit itself to the female. If he goes about his duties properly, her excitement increases. Finally, when she is ready for the insertion of the male organ, he will discover that his usual period is considerably extended and that he can maintain the rhythmic motion for a longer interval before being forced to reduce his pace. He can with greater ease delay his orgasm to a time more in keeping with his partner's need for satisfaction, and the woman's enjoyment can be heightened considerably. The degree of control he must practice on this occasion is very slight compared with that which he must generally exert when he is highly stimulated; the brain has not been too much involved. The result is that he behaves automatically, and control takes care of itself.

The same condition will manifest itself if he assumes the underneath position, since the physical factor contributing the most to his orgasm is the amount of genital movement the male exerts, whether he be inserted or not. Any man knows it is possible to bring about orgasm simply be moving his organ against the vulva, the stomach, or between the female breasts, if he maintains the friction long enough. Frequently, he even finds it necessary to move his organ when it is held in the female hand, so inexpert may she be in this matter.

In this position, the male has only to lie relaxed, studying and enjoying the development or extent of his partner's passion; or if this becomes too stimulating, centering his attention on other things, perhaps running over in his mind the events of the day. When the woman has completely satisfied herself, he can then, without shifting his position, and with deep penetrating, lifting thrusts, almost swooningly pleasurable to a highly passionate woman, bring about his own orgasm. Unfortunately, some men do not care for this position. This however, should be of little importance to an adequate lover, since his emotions are the less important of the two.

Liquor has an inconsistent influence on sexual behavior in that sometimes it will heighten passion, particularly in women, and at other times lower it, depending upon the quantity absorbed and the mood of the individual. However, a man who has consumed a favorable quantity under agreeable circumstances will discover that he can perform an adequate sex act. Alcohol seems to have a dulling effect upon the penis, at times limiting the rigidity of erection and giving it a certain pliability. When the male organ is in a state of limp erection, orgasm is not so readily attained as when erection is intense. Many women prefer this condition when it can be achieved.

However, it must be noted that, under some circumstances, overindulgence in alcohol may lead to temporary impotence. More than one bridegroom has discovered, to his embarrassment on his wedding night, that he was unable to perform his marital function. Under any circumstances, it is a dangerous practice to utilize the unpredictable effects of alcohol for the purpose of developing sexual staying power.

The average man finds it difficult to delay his climax primarily because of the fact that he engages in intercourse only when he is very much in the mood. His desire may have started even while he was at work or early in the evening, and he goes through hours of expectation with his imagination highly stimulated. Consequently, he is well on the road to orgasm after only a few minutes of foreplay.

Another source of trouble is that many couples do not engage in intercourse with sufficient frequency. The best and most successful relationship is by no means always that which the male anticipates. Frequently it results in a complete failure, caused by the fact that he is too stimulated to exercise the necessary control. The act is completed too quickly for both partners. People do not eat only when they are starving, nor do they sleep only when exhausted. Why, then, should a man make love to his wife only when he is in an advanced state of sexual excitement? The unpremeditated, relaxed session is often more enjoyable than the tense, pent-up, explosive interval, and frequent love-making conditions self-control.

The problem of developing self-control should be an easy one for those men who practice *coitus interruptus,* the habit of withdrawing the male organ just prior to orgasm as a birth-control method. In regarding it as a menace to the mental and physical well-being of both men and women, the medical profession assumes that many a man withdraws before his partner is satisfied and consequently leaves her in a trouble state, mentally and physically. It is true that such a constant process may undermine her health.

On the other hand, if a man is forced to resort to it, but only after the female is first thoroughly gratified, the practice cannot be injurious to a woman. When consistently engaged in, it is decidedly harmful to the male. Occasional indulgence will not, however, have deleterious results.

However, from the standpoint of pure enjoyment, *coitus interruptus* is most unsatisfactory. A man experiences a serious mental and physical strain in determining the precise moment to withdraw. This inevitably interferes with his pleasure, and he suffers a feeling of depression and incompleteness when orgasm occurs following withdrawal. But, since this technique necessitates the most rigorous self-control, any man who practices it can easily bring into play the less stringent requirements necessary to achieve delayed orgasm.

A brief word should be devoted to another condition which, while not too common, can be most disturbing to an individual afflicted by it. It is a sexual impotence which can occur at indeterminate periods when the male has been denied constant sexual society over a long interval or even at a time when his sex life is following a perfectly normal routine.

This condition is just the reverse of an undelayable orgasm and presents itself in the inability of the male to develop erection. He may have a definite desire for intercourse, but despite his emotion the penis cannot attain rigidity. He may find himself perfectly competent with one woman and helplessly inadequate with another. His sexual nature is not involved, for a male of moderate passion can become just as much a victim of the disorder as one of violent emotion. It occurs frequently when a man finds himself sexually engaged with a woman for the first time, but it can occur with his wife if his excitement is excessive. On such occasions, no amount of genital play can bring the penis to a rigid state.

Many men beset by this unpredictable inconvenience are terrified by the thought that their virility is beginning to dwindle; that they are victims of premature impotence. Such a belief has no foundation. Some youths of twenty are as much afflicted as is a man of fifty, and the sexual potential of the latter is far from exhausted at that age.

This constant fear of vanishing sexual energy gradually assumes a paramount importance in the victim's mind, and he expects every sexual session to terminate in frustration. This results in continuous mental uneasiness which, unfortunately, aggravates the affliction.

Where this condition is not the result of organic changes, which should be determined by medical consultation, it is purely psychological, and a man is foolish to torture himself with the specter of impotence. Constant sexual association of a compatible nature will frequently eliminate this disturbance. But when it persists, it requires hypno-therapy or psychiatric treatment, not because the individual is a mental case, but because the root of the trouble is located in some mental distortion. The psychiatrist will track it down, adjust it to the shape of truth, and give it its proper value. He will eventually succeed in convincing his patient that he is perfectly normal physically and establish self-confidence. Were it possible for the sexually harassed male to realize this at the outset, the condition would in all probability take care of itself.

But with respect to the most prominent problem, the undelayed orgasm, it is strongly recommended that a man so annoyed start experimenting immediately with the woman-above position. Once he has achieved the ability to postpone climax, he will develop a self-confidence which works psychologically upon his ability to operate from any position. This matter of control, whether it be "self" or "automatic" should be strictly pursued by every man who loves his wife and strives to keep her physically, mentally, and healthfully happy.

14.

Theory of the Safe Days

THE operation of the menstrual cycle is a phenomenon with which scarcely one woman in ten is thoroughly familiar, although it is a regular function of their daily lives. An understanding of it may aid those couples who, due to faulty timing, fail to bring about impregnation, or contrariwise, find it desirable to reduce it.

It is interesting to notice that as recently as approximately twenty years ago the details of the phenomenon of the menstrual flow were not completely understood by the medical profession. We may avoid a description of all the lengthy, patient, scientific research which went into the study and concentrate on what is generally accepted.

It is known that the female egg or ovum ripens in an ovary cavity known as the Graafian follicle. When the egg matures fully, fifteen days preceding menstruation, the follicle bursts, allowing the egg to enter the Fallopian tube. This process is known as "ovulation." The egg must be fertilized by the male sperm within a few hours after ovulation; otherwise the egg perishes. Since the precise moment of ovulation cannot be determined, twenty-four hours are allowed for fertilization, although it occurs in less time, perhaps in the neighborhood of four. The male sperm can maintain its fertilizing vigor at best for only two days after entering the female body, but it can live considerably longer.

It is known also that the pituitary gland, located in the brain, does, among other functions, create activity of the uterus. The day following ovulation, a group of cells called the "yellow body" comes into being on the ovary, nullifies the control of the pituitary over the uterus, and instructs it to relax and adjust itself to the arrival of the egg by taking on increased supplies of blood.

Finally, in order to develop normally, the fertilized ovum must imbed itself in the wall of the uterus. This can be accomplished only when the uterus is quiet and the membrane relaxed.

Now that we understand the basic facts, let us see how pregnancy takes place, or how, failing impregnation, a menstrual flow occurs.

Ovulation takes place fifteen days before a period and the egg starts a journey through the Fallopian tube. It must be speedily fertilized or it dies. The day following ovulation, the yellow body materializes on the ovary and starts to exert its influence over the uterus by commanding quiet and directing nourishing stores of blood to it.

Unfortunately for women, the yellow body automatically issues its instructions to the uterus on the assumption that a fertilized egg will arrive there. However, should the ovum perish by reason of nonfertilization, the yellow body realizes this only ten days later, and then starts to deteriorate. By the fourteenth day, it has disappeared, whereupon the pituitary, once again in control, induces contractions in the uterus, causing it to dislodge a lining consisting of excess blood and mucus. The female thus experiences the beginning of the menstrual flow.

If, however, a fertilized ovum arrives at the uterus and successfully attaches itself, the yellow body reacts differently and retains control until the beginning of labor, when the pituitary again takes command, causing the contractions of the womb which expel the child.

These principles make it obvious that a woman can conceive only within twenty-four hours or less following the ovulation which occurs on the fifteenth day prior to menstruation. This day, then, is not "safe." Furthermore, since

FRONTAL VIEW OF FEMALE REPRODUCTIVE SYSTEM

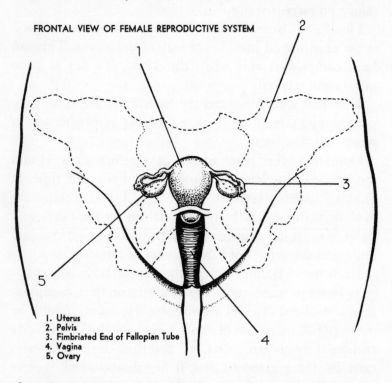

1. Uterus
2. Pelvis
3. Fimbriated End of Fallopian Tube
4. Vagina
5. Ovary

the spermatozoa can remain vigorous for forty-eight hours, it is apparent that intercourse occuring one or two days prior to ovulation is "dangerous" because the sperm, still alive and potent, may be waiting for the egg at time of ovulation. Thus, the seventeenth and sixteenth days before menstruation are likewise "unsafe."

Consequently, conception appears theoretically to be

possible only from relationships occurring on the seventeenth, sixteenth, or fifteenth day prior to ovulation; all other days in the cycle should be "safe." If a woman has a cycle of twenty-six days and a menstrual period of five days, she has eighteen days during which she can feel free from impregnation. That is the basis of the theory of the rhythm. However, there are complications to be considered.

First of all, this theory applies only to a woman with a constant twenty-six-day cycle, who knows beyond doubt that she is precisely that regular. Suppose, however, that she ovulates two days sooner or later; no medical man will deny this possibility. If she ovulates two days earlier than usual or seventeen days before her period instead of fifteen, she is susceptible to impregnation by intercourse occurring on the nineteenth, eighteenth, or seventeenth day before her period. Failing this, her flow will start two days earlier. If, on the other hand, she ovulates two days later than usual, or on the thirteenth day prior to the normal date of her period, then intercourse on the fifteenth, fourteenth, or thirteenth day subjects her to the possibility of pregnancy. Barring this, her period will fall two days late.

It must be borne in mind that a woman has only her past regularity to depend upon, and that no one can state positively that this regularity will continue. The fact is, it will not. Nor is it possible to determine the exact date of ovulation except by consulting a record of previous periods, since it can be established only by going back fifteen days from the *last* day of the cycle.

It seems obvious that if we add two days to each side of the original three dangerous days, increasing them now to the nineteenth, eighteenth, seventeenth, sixteenth, fifteenth, fourteenth, and thirteenth we have made an allowance for any future irregularity of the ovulation date. This is advisable under any circumstances and advocates of the rhythm themselves suggest it.

However, although we have allowed for an irregularity of two days in either direction, no one can guarantee against the future possibility of a three, four, or five-day irregularity. This unexpectedly happens to many women, and the discrepancy can obtain for as long a period as a week or more. To be reasonably safe, we may add four days on each side of the original three danger days as a more than sufficient allowance for a system which is presumed to operate with far greater scientific consistency. The questionable days now represent the twenty-first, twentieth, nineteenth, eighteenth, seventeenth, sixteenth, fifteenth, fourteenth, thirteenth, twelfth, and eleventh days before the usual termination of the next period. Now, in a theretofore regular cycle of twenty-six days, five days of which include menstruation, with eleven days questionable, a woman can feel reasonably safe for ten days.

Although this allowance of an extra four days is considerably more than that regarded as necessary by one of the research scientists principally responsible for this enlightening discovery, it still may not be enough. Nature is far too unreliable, and many unexpected happenings may occur to alter a previously regular menstrual cycle: a fall, a blow, a shock, an illness, a psychological explosion, an accident, a change of climate or overstimulation. If a shock can bring about an abortion or miscarriage, it is not inconceivable that it may cause a contraction of the ovary and force the Graafian follicle to expel an egg prematurely.

On the other hand, an egg may precociously mature far

ahead of its time. Since the Graafian cavities and their contents have been developed since adolescence and perhaps at birth, it is not impossible for an individual egg to mature weeks in advance or a retarded one, weeks later.

Furthermore, the authorities advise that before applying this principle, the regularity of the menstrual cycle be carefully recorded and observed for at least a year, and for an additional four or five months following any subsequent disruption, in order to determine whether it occurs with absolute consistency. Obviously, they also recognize the possibility of occasional irregularity.

In addition, it is perfectly possible that nature, which is known to play unexpected pranks, may decide to release eggs from both ovaries at different intervals during the same cycle instead of the customary single egg. In fact, fraternal twins have been born whose relationship was that of half-brothers. Each had a different father. Nor can anyone say how frequently a pair of eggs are released at different intervals, because a relationship may not have taken place at the time one or the other was expelled.

A girl who marries at twenty has roughly twenty-five years before the menopause. Calculated at the rate of twelve cycles a year, although there will be more, she undergoes in that span three hundred cycles which we may further reduce by eighteen while she bears two children. It is not farfetched to assume that out of the remaining two hundred and eighty-two cycles, nature may deviate at least half a dozen times. If pregnancy ensues as the result of only three of the six occasions, the family has been unexpectedly increased.

While it is absolutely true that many people operate under the rhythm principle to their satisfaction, others have failed to find it reliable. It may be argued, of course, that the latter were careless in their application, but they deny it.

There is also some difference of opinion among the authorities themselves; some state that ovulation definitely takes place only on the fifteenth day preceding the end of the next period, while others assert that it may occur on any one of five consecutive days. Although both sides have ample evidence to support their contentions, the layman is unable to resolve the conflict.

The figures used are based on a woman with a simple twenty-six day cycle. Some women, however, experience a double cycle, such as twenty-six days one month, and twenty-eight days the next. Still others are subject to a triple cycle of twenty-six, twenty-eight, and thirty days over a period of three months. While it is not difficult to work out a table to meet these situations, since only the extremes are considered, it requires too much calculation, the results of which still offer questionable security. This is, of course, a matter of opinion.

However, one reliable and valuable fact exists, if the present explanation of the menstrual cycle is accepted. A specific period encouraging impregnation has been determined. And it can be utilized or avoided depending upon the desire for a family.

It is appropriate to discuss briefly at this point the practicability of engaging in intercourse during a mentrual period. Beyond the inconvenience of it, there is no healthful reason why it shouldn't be practiced. It will neither lengthen nor decrease the flow as many women believe.

Furthermore, a great proportion of females acquire their strongest sexual urges at this time. Since the first and last day of the period are usually characterized by a slight staining only, a relationship, then, is not too disagreeable. However, should a wife indicate any reluctance to engage on these occasions, no husband should insist upon it.

This must not be construed to mean that a wife has no duty or responsibility during this period to satisfy her husband's sexual needs. Many women flow the better part of a week, and this is a long interval for a man to practice self control. A thoughtful and devoted mate will not ignore her husband's sexual moods at this time. On the contrary, she will take pains to anticipate and satisfy them, if need be, by adequate means at her disposal.

Should she be one of those women whose periods are attended by pain and discomfort, naturally, no obligation exists. But barring this, any indifference to her husband's feeling is inexcusable. Considerations of this type on the part of both partners provide the kind of home atmosphere that cements marriage ties and encourages general compatibility.

15.

Sexual Incompatibility

FREQUENT letters are received commenting upon the subject matter of the author's previous books. For the most part they come from educated readers of comfortable circumstances who thank us for giving the public an informative text on a subject about which, heretofore, little of practical value has been written for the layman.

Since these communications are usually the same in tone, it may prove advantageous to quote one of these in paraphrased form, a precaution taken to protect the identity of the sender. Readers will then see that others are confronted with their identical problems.

Gentlemen:

Your publisher has been requested to send you this letter. Actually, I cannot improve on what has already been printed on the jacket of your book.

Since I have been married nearly 20 years, I am hardly a youth, but I believe a person is never too old to learn.

Unfortunately, it is impossible for the average man to size up the sexual qualities of his future wife as he can her intellectual and social ones, all of which have a definite bearing on the success of matrimony.

Throughout many of the long years of my marriage, I tried to excuse the lack of sexual harmony existing between us on the grounds that I must give my wife time to get used to the idea of sexual relationships; that, perhaps, it was my fault. But this philosophy is no longer valid. She is passive, unresponsive, but dutiful. Experimentation in our early wedded life was disagreeable to her. Occasionally, just before a period, a satisfactory relationship occurs. But this is a rare event.

I have been forced to conclude finally that I am not to blame, just as I have been forced occasionally to take up with temporary mistresses. These relationships were always satisfactory to both parties. I never maintained them over prolonged periods, because I would do nothing to disturb my marriage. But during these intervals a varied sexual activity was engaged in, and I discovered oral connection to be a common practice with women with any degree of passion. This is out of the question with my wife. What little response she has is purely conventional.

I know I have remained with her all these years because I love her. She is a good mother and housewife. But as a sweetheart, she is a failure.

I know too, there are others in the world in the same position I am. Being a traveling man, I have discussed the situation many times in an evening spent in a hotel lobby. We are unfortunates with no sexual compatibility in our lives as may be found in other partnerships. Occasionally, now, I still seek diversion. Even "Call Girls" have certain charms that undoubtedly only too many wives could adopt for the betterment of home life. My present feeling toward my wife is largely one of obligation for having spent so many years with me.

Thank you for the contents of your book. Many others, I know, have gained as much from reading it as I have. Perhaps sexual compatibility can only come with the right girl at the right time."

This is a tragic letter, made more so by the unnecessary circumstances that led up to it. Although it is probably now too late for an adjustment it was not too late in the beginning.

Clearly the writer is an educated man, a decent man with good ethical standards, a respect for his wife, and a strong regard for the obligations of matrimony. Only those who are either naive or live an unnatural existence will criticize his occasional philanderings. It has been forced upon him as it would be forced upon most men given similar opportunities. There is no point in saying he should have withstood temptations of the flesh. The flesh has been made purposely weak to combat abstention in this respect and assure the perpetuation of the race. Furthermore, a craving that remains unsatisfied day after day must eventually seek satisfaction.

In our younger years sexual hunger plays a dominant role in our lives. It is a constant force to be controlled rather than destroyed. Control is intended. It is too powerful a factor not to require some measure of restraint. We read constantly in newspaper headlines what occurs when sex runs amuck. The result is rape and murder. Consequently, everyone, regardless of sexual demands must exercise a definite control over his impulses. But this does not mean suppression. It merely means intelligent restraint, which can be imposed in various ways without interfering too greatly with sexual gratification.

It must never be assumed that the author regards the sexual urge as the major factor in a matrimonial partnership. Most important by far is the spiritual element. This pronouncement is made not for the purpose of seeking ecclesiastical approval but because it is absolute fact. The writer of the foregoing letter himself proves this when he says, "I know I have remained with her all these years because I love her." Even a serious complaint of almost twenty years duration, hasn't sufficient strength to force him to abandon a good and faithful wife, though, perhaps, a thoughtless one. Had he been a less determined man, as too many men are, his marriage would have dissolved long ago.

But next to the spiritual, the need for sexual gratification is the most powerful secondary factor in our lives. It bears the relationship of oil to gasoline in the operation of a car. An automobile can run longer without oil than gas. But eventually the lack of a lubricant will impose it's penalty. Something snaps or burns, and the car is halted despite a full tank of fuel—the major ingredient.

No reader should make the mistake of thinking that the foregoing letter represents an isolated case. Nor should one delude himself or herself into believing that it typifies no more than a tiny fraction of matrimonial relationships. The letter speaks for the condition existing in the majority of marriages, marriages held together only by economic necessity. Divorce is expensive.

How, then, does a couple go about correcting this unfortunate suituation? They start by taking for granted at the very outset of marriage that sooner or later the powerful urge of sex will introduce serious complications into their wedded life; complications often sufficient to bring about divorce. They start also by realizing that the perfect marriage is rare—so rare, in fact, it is no exaggeration to say that total harmony is non-existent. No one, absolutely no one, can state truthfully that five, ten, fifteen, or fifty years of wedded life has failed to manufacture some sort of friction serious enough to create periods of deep unhappiness.

But in addition to the friction resulting entirely from human contrariness, other types of irritations intrude and further complicate married life. It may be another man or woman, the mortgage, the old car, a problem child, the loss of a job, or a hundred other ills. All these can and do upset the balance of domestic harmony and lead to acts of inconsideration that would not occur but for such outside problems. When all of these various influences are combined, it is not at all surprising that divorce or separation assumes alarming proportions. Nor is too much imagination required to approximate the more stupendous increase that would result, finances permitting.

The marriage ceremony anticipates something of the grimness of the future when both hopefuls swear before God to take each other "for better, for worse; for richer, for poorer; in sickness and in health; until death do them part." It contains no optimistic phrases or sentiments. It is a matter of vows. Human experience has revealed the marriage path to be an uncertain one; so uncertain, in fact, that those traveling over it are forced by oath to remain together.

Closely bound together by matrimony, then, are two inter-dependent forces—spiritual love and sexual love. Regarding the spiritual, no established rules can be set down to cover every specific act in which we may engage. We may find ourselves at some time involved in undreamed-of situations. But with respect to the sexual side of our lives, the solution is far simpler. Definite complications can be anticipated and a procedure prescribed that will prevent their occurrence.

Consequently, regardless of the optimism and certainty with which everyone faces the altar, the newly wedded couple must reconcile themselves to the fact that sooner or later one partner will sexually fail the other unless immediate steps are taken to prevent it. In most instances the wife will disappoint the husband, particularly in later years. It is, therefore, the male's first step to adapt his wife to the sexual environment that will constantly surround her. His failure to do this makes him fully responsible for any sexual incompatibility that may subsequently enter his married life. The writer of the foregoing letter evidently neglected to do this.

But no criticism attaches to him. In his youth, he lacked the knowledge born of experience. But what youth has it? What youth can have it? A boy's parents are probably as ignorant of the facts of life as the son. More than likely the father, himself, is a victim of sexual discontent. If so, he is either reluctant to discuss the matter with his boy, or feels his case is an exception to the general belief that most marriages are sexual successes—when they are, in fact, sexual failures. Furthermore, there are no adequate educational courses on the subject; nor are there adequate texts for the laymen.

Consequently, it is to be expected that any youth will take for granted that a sexual relationship, because it is a universal indulgence, is also a mechanical one. This ignorance is the root of the evil. On the contrary, satisfactory sexual association requires thoroughly scientific practices if any degree of permanent harmony is to follow.

There are warnings all along the road of matrimony. Not only must one be able to read them; he or she must also be able to anticipate them. It is not a picturesque highway. The plan of it never varies. Of course, certain side roads run off here and there, but these can be ignored. We are concerned only with the route taken by the vast majority of travelers. We will follow that road, observe its warnings, and pursue it safely to its end.

It must be realized that man and woman are for the most part, direct opposites. Not only are the two words themselves antonyms, but in their relationship man and woman stand in marked contrast to each other. Physically, man is strong, woman is weak. Intellectually, man is logical, woman is emotional. Morally, man is loose, woman is strict. Spiritually, man is hard, woman is soft. In the selection of other categories, it is the man who pursues and woman who is pursued, the man who gambles and the woman who insists upon security, the man who provides the income, and the woman who runs the home. This is the pattern, a perfect system of check and balance. The exceptions do not count. Numerically, they are only a small percentage of the whole.

Since in all other relationships this matter of opposites holds true, it should be expected that the same formula obtains in sexual relationship. It does, and we find that man by nature requires active and constant association in the practice of sex, while a woman inclines toward passivity and eventual lack of interest. Nor is this deniable on any basis of knowledge. Looking at the animal kingdom we find that the bitch, the mare, the doe, to mention just a few, are only periodically in heat while the male of the specie knows no such limitation. This is, of course, precisely as nature intended it. The male has been selected to plant the seed at every opportunity. The perpetuation of the specie depends on it. Man and woman are not excepted.

Man, however, has been endowed with qualities and abilities not possessed by the lower orders. He is expected by the Creator to utilize these gifts for their intended purposes. Man must use judgment. But this alters neither man's nor woman's basic position in the scheme of things. Sexually, he is essentially active, she passive. This, of course, is as it should be. Were both man and woman constantly in a sexual mood, overpopulation would surely become a problem. Were they both equally restrained, underpopulation would result. But as it stands the system of check and balance follows through. Woman is the moderating influence.

It becomes obvious, then, that sooner or later a wife by

her very endowment is going to interpose a barrier to the sexual demands of her husband. It may or may not be beyond her control, it may be conscious or unconscious, it may be deliberate or unintentional. But unless a man is married to a member of the sexual minority, the average wife will eventually bring him periods of sexual disappointment.

With this certainty facing him, a man must for his own sake, as well as his wife's, take steps long before the occurrences to modify a situation he cannot altogether prevent. He must, in short, insure the fact that the sweetheart he married forever remains one, in addition to becoming a wife. Only the male can do this, because it is not within a woman's power. Indeed, there are certain definite obligations that a wife owes to her husband. But unless she is unusually intelligent and thoughtful, even these will be overlooked unless brought to her attention.

Let us stop on the road over which we are traveling, and study a common warning sign. It may be somewhat concealed because there is intent to conceal. A husband must be alert and watchful for it. It concern's a wife's reluctance to dress and undress before her husband. Since she herself feels a twinge of guilt at the undue embarrassment experienced on these occasions, she attempts to be casual about her actions. Consequently, her husband sees nothing suggestive in them. The fact that she consistently dresses and undresses in the bathroom, leads him to believe she simply prefers to leave her underclothes there. She might have remarked, originally that she finds the bathroom warmer in the morning. If so, he does not wonder why she takes her underclothing there during the summer or in the early evening when they are preparing to go out. At these times the house is quite comfortable. Or why she always happens to turn her back when changing a brassiere, or to take shelter behind a closet door when removing her undergarments.

Of course, being a woman this behavior pattern is more instinctive than otherwise. Woman is by nature modest. Normally, she is self-conscious regarding anything in conflict with this innate distaste for nudity.

This would be perfectly acceptable if it extended no further. But unfortunately it does. If a reserve is maintained with respect to simple nakedness, certainly more binding restraints are likely to be applied at times of even greater intimacy—sexual relations. Precisely what these may be can vary, and are treated elsewhere in the book. It is sufficient to say at this point, that undue modesty in a minor situation forecasts a still greater example of it in a major one. Regardless of how normal this reaction may be at ordinary times, measures must be taken immediately to nullify it. It should be done by having a heart-to-heart talk, and it is suggested that a direct approach in line with the following take place some evening when both parties are completely relaxed and intend to spend a quiet evening at home.

"Grace," the husband might say by way of introduction, "let's have a little talk about something, something very important. Okay?" Grace will probably say, "Sure, of course."

The husband then goes on. "Now I want you to be perfectly frank. That's the important thing, frankness. Don't say 'Yes' or 'No' to anything unless you honestly mean it. Promise?"

Grace will answer, "I promise. What's it all about?"

"Well," her husband continues, "Tell me exactly how you feel about sex, about sexual intercourse. Do you feel that it is indecent, even the least little bit. Now think carefully."

Grace, who will not want to admit even to herself that she is troubled at times, will ignore the request for frankness and say, "Of course, I don't feel it is indecent. It's a perfectly natural thing to engage in."

"That's really how you feel about it, is it?" her husband should go on. "You feel perfectly relaxed, perfectly at ease, not the slightest thing on your mind?"

Grace might hesitate very slightly at this point, so slightly that a hopeful mate might be inclined to overlook it, and then reply, "Well . . . yes. Why do you ask me?"

"I'll tell you in a minute. I just have a couple of more questions. How do you feel about nakedness, Grace. I mean in front of me. Does it embarass you?"

Grace will probably pause noticably this time. Then, if she has any intention of being frank, she will answer, "Well . . . yes it does."

Her husband then asks, "Why?"

"Well," Grace will probably reply, "I don't know exactly. I just feel funny about it."

"How?" persists her husband.

"Well," continues Grace, "I guess I'm just not used to going around without any clothes on in front of men."

"Yes, but I'm not 'men.' I'm your husband. After all, we don't have any physical secrets from each other. I know every square inch of you."

"I know," Grace will say, "But that's different. We're under the covers, the lights are out."

The husband continues. "But on our honeymoon the lights weren't always out. There were several afternoons. Remember?"

"Yes, but the covers were always up, if you remember."

The husband reflects and recalls that this is true.

"Well, Grace," he continues, "I'll tell you why I'm asking these questions. I don't care if you undress in the bathroom, or in the cellar, provided you have some other reason for it than just plain modesty. I'm not the gloating type, you know that."

Grace nods and her husband goes on. "I just want you to see sex in the right perspective, Grace. I don't want you to feel for an instant that anything we do in bed is wrong. I don't want you to feel that nakedness is indecent. There is nothing wrong whatever with any aspect of normal sex, and particularly between husband and wife. Take my word for it, Grace, there is nothing that you or I will do, that millions of other couples won't be doing."

"Well, I guess you're right."

"There's no guessing about it. Take the youngster. She doesn't hide behind the closet door or lock the bathroom everytime she takes a shower. She doesn't see anything wrong in walking around without any clothes on in front of her parents. She won't do it in front of anyone else, but she would be as selfconscious as you are right now if she were brought up to believe there is something indecent about a naked body. Do you follow me?"

"Yes."

"Let me ask you something else, Grace. How do you suppose this idea about nudity developed?"

"I don't know."

"It developed because of peoples' stupid idea concerning sex. Nudity is associated with sexual activity, and too many people always feel guilty when engaging in sex. It's as if they're doing something they're not supposed to do. Well, that's just as stupid. The very existance of the orgasm, the uncontrollable erection of the male, the sensitivity of the clitoris—all these things were created in us to make sure we'd have sexual relations. In other words we were trapped into it. Why should we fight it then? If nature were so opposed to it, she wouldn't have set this trap. That's only common sense, isn't it?"

"Well, yes."

"And while we're on the subject, let me ask you one more question. When we're having a relationship, do you let yourself go completely?"

"I suppose so. What do you mean?"

"I mean this. Do you try to keep from moaning or twisting too violently for fear that I might think it's strange, for fear that I might think you're over-sexed, for fear that I might think you are enjoying yourself too much?"

Grace might consider this question a few moments before answering. "Well, I suppose I do . . . sometimes."

"All right, Grace, then let's have an understanding right now. I don't ever want you to exert any self-control again. And you should know this too. There isn't a man who doesn't enjoy a passionate woman. The more passionate she is, the more he enjoys her. The more likely he is, too, not to run around with other women, because another woman won't have any more to offer him than his wife. Can you understand that?"

Grace nods, and her husband continues. "And while we're at it, Grace, let's get this straight, too. I don't hesitate to make my feelings known when I'm in a sexual mood. But if you restrain yourself, because of some ridiculous idea that it's unladylike to let me know when you feel the same, I won't be able to detect it. It's just as much your duty to let me know when you want to be loved as it is mine to love you. Is that clear?"

"Yes."

"I hope it is, Grace, I hope you're just not taking this as some routine conversation. It's a very serious matter, very serious. Much of our future happiness can depend on it."

How many young men, or any married men, have ever held such a conversation with their wives? What makes a man think that it isn't necessary? What makes him believe the average woman feels or should feel precisely the same about such matters as he? Only his assumption that because he does, she does.

On the other hand, if the average man devoted even half as much time in reaching an early understanding with his wife as he subsequently spends attempting to badger her into intercourse when she is disinclined, a far more satisfactory relationship would exist among married couples today and in the future.

This chapter deals only with the restraint imposed by women upon themselves: restraint resulting from society's general attitude toward the sexual relationship. Another chapter discusses specific experiences that may have created sexual apathy in a woman.

Why should conversation of this nature be held early in married life, and why is it basic? We discover this as we proceed further along the road we have been traveling. Grace and Walter are now two years older. Walter, however, neglected to have a discussion of the character previously suggested. During the interval, the novelty of sex, the desire for frequent engagement, has diminished considerably. In fact, now that her appetite has been satisfied time and time again, Grace in her off moods sees a certain sordidness in the sexual picture. Why can't she and Walter watch television without the inevitable running of his hand beneath her dress or beneath her brassiere This constant inclination of his to be always fooling around has a certain amount of crudeness to it.

The fact is that Walter is *not* always doing this. For him, too, but only as far as Grace is concerned, the original heat of the honeymoon has reduced itself, but to a less limited degree. Grace is a woman. It should be expected that her sexual ardor will gradually diminish, though not her devotion. During the first three or four months of marriage Walter would attempt to arouse his wife at least every other night and meet no objection. Now, he is adjusted to a four night interval or an occasional three. To Grace, however, the periods seem considerably shorter.

Walter observes disappointedly that Grace assumes the most uncooperative positions on the divan when she doesn't select one of the chairs. Nor does she seem to encourage his intimacies as frequently as she used to. She is now very definite about saying, "Turn out the light, Walter." She never fails to wear her pajama pants and lay on her side as soon as she strikes the pillow. "It's not as easy to get at Grace at it used to be," muses Walter, but he still attributes much of it to coincidence. After all, when he is really aroused she cooperates satisfactorily enough.

Fifteen years pass; the travelers are now well along the road. They have a son of nine, daughters of twelve and three. For some reason Walter has not kept pace with the optimistic dreams of his youth. He isn't earning any more or any less than his neighbors, and, like them, he can't afford a maid for Grace. The girls seem to need more clothes than can reasonably be afforded, so Grace is always making something or other. The older youngsters get along just like any other brother and sister, and Grace's nerves are frequently worn thin from their constant bickering. Too often Walter finds a short-tempered wife when he returns from the plant in the evening. By the time the youngest child is asleep and the others quarrel their way to bed, Grace is so thoroughly exhausted, she can hardly wait to turn in.

But Walter is not without his aggravations. He's disgusted with office politics and far from happy with his salary. Many an evening he'd like nothing better than to relax with Grace in one of their more tender moods of former years. He knows, though, that she is tired and irritable, and he reflects upon the many times that this is the situation. Besides she no longer responds as readily to sexual stimulation. A woman must be both mentally and physically rested before she becomes susceptible to excitation. Walter meditates upon the infrequency of these occasions. Once in a while, following some social gathering and a few drinks, Grace does behave as in their early married life. But these are rare instances. Walter wonders what has happened and whether this state of affairs will continue. He is now only forty. Even at fifty he will still be vigorous sexually.

We follow the road for these ten years. Grace is now 48. Walter has finally attained a certain measure of financial security, but hardly in keeping with his once bright hopes. Their older daughter is married, the son is away at college, the youngest about to enter high school. At last Walter has managed to create a somewhat satisfactory sex life for himself. Of course, it does not revolve around Grace. A comfortable and sexually active widow of perhaps 38 now provides Walter with the type of society his wife denied him. Grace herself is still far from elderly. She accommodates Walter's less frequent amative demands with greater tolerance now that she has been relieved of the pure drudgery of the previous ten years. But it is a mechanical relationship. Grace is sexually apathetic. Indeed, given her choice, she would prefer to avoid sex entirely. Only a belated sense of duty motivates her on these infrequent occasions.

We must face it. This is the road most married couples travel on their sexual journey. Dull, unpicturesque, pitted with frustrations, alive with perilous possibilities. The solution lies in an alternate road; one with sturdy embankments that resist landslides, and firm paving that refuses to succumb to washouts. A wedded pair is well on this road when they reach the understanding previously discussed. Some men will, of course, insist and be absolutely right, that their wives at no time during the early period of their marriages ever showed the slightest reluctance to undress or appear in the nude. Nevertheless, these husbands will claim that their wives are cold today.

This can be perfectly true, but the germ of excess modesty was always lurking within those women precisely as it lurks in a varying degree in every woman, including the most brazen prostitute. But there is a reason why it did not make itself manifest immediately. First, one must consider the impression that most people have regarding intercourse; the impression that society as well as the home has forced upon them; the impression that *all sexual relationship* is indecent. Even the press enjoys nothing better than the opportunity to release news, the major ingredient of which is adultery or sexual intimacy of some type. Heads shake throughout the world at the appalling thought that "X" spent a certain night in bed with "Y". Of course, heads should shake, though not by reason of any sexual element involved, but because protected sexual machines lack the good taste to indulge their appetites privately.

We read of street walkers, and expensive call girls. It

seems that these depraved creatures indulge in sexual intercourse! It makes no difference that if the reader asked why sexual relationship is a revolting activity, he would not receive an intelligent answer. The hypocrisies of our society do not permit it.

Think carefully before answering the following questions. Where has one read, or who has ever been told, that sexual intercourse, under any circumstances is a proper, necessary, healthy, normal function, and the principal objective of nature? Where does one read or hear that sexual intercourse was intended for pleasure, as well as perpetuation; otherwise, why the provision for the orgasm, the most delightful of all sensations? Most of us, if not everyone, will find difficulty in producing a shred of evidence giving wholehearted approval to the sex act. Parents approach the subject with embarrassment. One can hear the echo of a mother's voice advising her daughter, "So, Evelyn, as John's wife, you will owe him your sexual society. This is your wifely obligation."

Indeed, a most intelligent observation and a laudable sentiment, but why instill in the mind of a girl that the sex act is merely a debt due her future husband and not also a pleasure? Why not say something like this?

"So, Evelyn, do not hesitate at any time to make your sexual desires known to John, as he will make them known to you. It is the most delightful of all physical relationships, so enjoy it while you have the youth for it. You won't have it always."

No mother talks in this vein to her daughter. She is, herself, oppressed with guilt and fearful less the girl assume that she, her mother, enjoys a healthy sex life. The entire discussion is laden with apology for a union that is the consummation of the love and devotion of two persons for each other.

How, then, can any husband expect a wife to come to him always relaxed in her mind if she considers intercourse an act to be engaged in only at times of overwhelming passion, or strictly as a duty! Yet, deep within the subconscious of almost every woman, if not active in the conscious, is this unhealthy attitude toward sexual enjoyment for its own sake.

If, then, she appears in the early periods of marriage to be without certain inhibitions, it is only because the novelty of intimacy and passions not yet thoroughly appeased have temporarily buried her doubts, much in the manner than a man will rationalize murder in the heat of anger and deplore it in the sober light of reaction.

Therefore, no husband can allow himself to be misled by initial sexual abandonment on the part of his wife, nor should she allow herself to be deceived by her earlier physical reactions and assume that the future will be a continuous series of excitedly awaited sexual climaxes. She, as well as he, must realize that the early stage of marriage is only temporary. She must condition herself to recall the fact, if a fact it is, that their previous relationship was by no means unpleasant to her. Strangely, prior sexual associations are to the average woman similar to labor pains. Both are quickly forgotten.

On the other hand, it is up to the husband to draw these facts to her attention and to provide the stimulation that will make their future sex life, at least, a perfectly agreeable one, if not an existence of continuous sensuality. In this word "agreeable" is the crux of the matter. This is the most the average married man can hope to accomplish. To do this, he must be a capable lover, and capability is not inherent. It must be acquired. A husband need only follow the procedures outlined here as he would a blue print, to insure the fact that, regardless of his wife's sexual make-up, his performance will be beyond criticism.

At this point the following question may arise: if, as the author has asserted, a woman's sexual feeling is fore-ordained to diminish, how can anyone prevent the operation of a seemingly fixed natural law? The answer is this: it is done by conditioning. If, from the time of marriage, sexual intercourse can be recalled by a wife always as a pleasant experience, no reason exists to avoid it. Even though her need for satisfaction is no longer as strong as her husband's, she has been conditioned to realize that proper stimulation will arouse her beyond the point of apathy and to actual desire. If, however, always occupying the forepart of her mind, is the half-guilty feeling that some illicit, degrading, impure, or unholy act is being committed, it is easy to see that only apathy and actual distaste will result.

If, then, we combine with this, a crude, selfish sexual performance by a sexually uneducated husband; one with careless habits of personal cleanliness, or whose desire is inflamed on occasion by drunkenness—who can fail to understand the increasing dislike for sexual union by an already indifferent wife?

It might be well to emphasize a condition of which, thanks to advertising, everyone should be conscious, but yet at times will overlook. Chronic bad breath, the cause of which is unknown and for which there is no cure at the present time, regardless of what one hears, can obviously impose a barrier to sexual enjoyment. Whether it be chronic or periodic, it is probable that all of us are offenders now and then, because the condition is no respecter of persons. Unfortunately, we may not be aware of it unless told; and everyone, even husband and wife, shares a reluctance to inform in this respect. Between marriage partners, however, it should be pointed out for the good of both.

In summary, the continuous fulfillment of a man's sexual needs can be achieved only when every vestige of sexual self-consciousness is entirely divorced from his mate, and when his technique in the *art* of sexual intercourse is perfect—because it is an art. Unless a woman can be conditioned to a complete abandonment of all inhibitions, no amount of mastery by her husband with regard to sexual procedure is sufficient to guarantee him a life of complete sexual harmony.

16.

Sexual Readjustment

NOW that the underlying reasons for sexual incompatibility have been detailed, those about to marry or who are in the stage immediately following marriage, can build a more substantial sexual future.

But this leaves the question as to how a man can relieve the sexual frustrations surrounding his home life after years of marriage; how he may instill some physical warmth in a wife whom he believes is cold. Lest such a husband confuse the terms, it should be repeated, although it appears elsewhere, that a "cold" woman is not necessarily a "frigid" woman. A woman is described as "cold" only when she is difficult to arouse. A "frigid" woman cannot be aroused under any circumstances.

Before any active attempt is made to resolve the problem, a husband must first analyze the situation with complete honesty. Self-pity cannot enter into it; he must offer no excuses for himself. Nor must he attempt to ease his disappointment by placing undue responsibility upon his wife. His answers to the following questions must be sincere.

1. Do I love my wife apart from my sexual need of her?
2. Would I miss her companionship?
3. Were I to lose her, would I truly be grief stricken?

4. Were she to die, do I feel at this moment I would not wish to remarry?

5. Do I thoroughly understand my wife's sexual disposition and needs?

6. Am I performing the sex act capably?

7. Do I require sexual gratification only with normal frequency?

8. Are my requirements entirely conventional with respect to the expressed—though not privately held —opinion of society?

9. Is my wife sincerely devoted to me?

10. Does she miss me when we're separated?

11. Is she a satisfactory mate in all respects other than sexual?

12. Were I to die tonight, would she really be grief stricken?

13. In the event of my death, do I believe she would wish to remain single?

14. On any occasions of sexual intimacy, does she display any signs of passion?

15. Does she exchange kiss for kiss?

16. Does she ever during a relationship voluntarily touch the male genitals?

Of course, we know from having read the previous chapter, that if a wife is cold or indifferent to sex, mistakes of omission or commission have already been made. The answers to the foregoing questions will simply indicate whether some degree of adjustment is possible at such a late date.

Regarding questions 1 through 4, the answers in each case must be an unqualified "Yes," if a man is to be considered completely in love with his wife and entitled to his wife's sexual services. "No" to any question indicates clearly that his wife is not involved in his finer emotions and exists principally in his life as a sexual instrument. Since this is the case, he can be certain his wife is quite aware of the minor position she holds. As a result, a psychological block has been created that will either affect any unrestricted abandonment by her in their sexual relations, or will conclude in feelings of bitterness at her weakness in giving any vent to her passion. This determines her to be less attainable when her husband next approaches her.

Unless the woman is the victim of overwhelming sexual excitability, or helplessly in love with the man, she cannot fail to resent the fact that her devotion is not equally returned. But since these types are not representative of the average woman, they do not qualify for discussion here.

Consequently, only one course remains for the man who wishes full sexual cooperation from his wife. He must convince her that he fully reciprocates her affection. Otherwise she will be nothing more to him than a machine responding to duty.

Questions 5 and 6 also require the answer "Yes" and with absolute knowledge of its truth. Regarding question 6, no man can be certain he is performing satisfactorily unless thoroughly familiar with his wife's sexual needs. These must be determined through conversation as well as observation and experimentation. Among other things, a wife should be asked unfailingly at the close of every sexual session whether she has been thoroughly satisfied or is capable of succeeding orgasms. If a man is at all doubtful of the answer to question number 6, he is, indeed, a poor one to complain of sexual apathy on the part of his wife.

In connection with questions 7 and 8, if the answer to either or both, is "Yes," it is unfortunate for the husband involved. He has no choice but to exercise self-control and reconcile himself to the type of sexual relationship preferred by his wife. Neither a man nor woman can be expected to engage in sexual activity more often than is reasonable. What constitutes a reasonable interval varies with the natures of individuals. Following several years of marriage, and barring unusual circumstances, such as long separations, a reasonable interval may be considered as no more than every 3rd day and no less than every 4th. For the average couple up to middle age once or twice a week is the usual frequency. No wife is justified in complaining of demands based upon a once-a-week period, provided no other objection than frequency enters into it.

With reference to question 8, this book is quite specific as to what constitutes normal sexual desires or behaviors. Notwithstanding that certain indulgences are perfectly normal, such as oral rhythm, if a woman objects to them no man can find in this a reasonable cause of complaint. Although such practices may be more exciting to him, they are in no way essential to his gratification; the male is the most easily and readily appeased of the species. It is a strange and abnormal spouse, indeed, who provided with other outlets for sexual relief must insist upon behaviors that are distasteful to his wife. Insistence upon these forms of relationship can only create a pronounced aversion to intimacy in his wife, and encourage an apathy that will eventually develop without help.

Notwithstanding the answers to the previous questions, 9, 10, 11, and 12 must be given an unqualified "Yes" if any hope exists for an adjustment of sexual differences. Unless a husband receives his wife's *entire* share of spiritual affection, he cannot hope to obtain her sexual love. No woman completely devoted to her mate can experience sexual desire for any other man provided she is given the constant society of her husband. If a woman, any woman, is repeatedly neglected over lengthy periods of time, constant association with a man who fills her needs will eventually convert the most faithful wife into the most devoted mistress. The male can more easily divide his affections, because nature intended he should. A woman can be loyal only to one man at a time.

Question 13 should receive a "Yes" answer, at least so far as the moment is concerned. A widow left unprovided for, and with two or three dependent youngsters, should remarry for economic expediency if nothing else. But at the time of her husband's death a devoted mate wil' feel than no man can ever replace him; that even want could not force her to consort with another. This, of course, is impractical. Time, happily, will dull the edge of her sorrow and force her to view the matter reasonably. Regardless, however, these feelings should be alive at the outset.

At the time of her husband's passing the same sentiments should be present even in a young and childless widow. But neither God, society, nor a thoughtful husband would expect that she spend her many future years in loneliness and physical frustration. This matter always should be discussed by married couples, the intention being to extract mutual promises that either will remarry in the event of the other's death. This understanding would give piece of mind to the surviving partner should he or she meet another and fall in love.

Questions 14, 15, 16 require "Yes" answers, if the possibility of adjustment is to receive further encouragement. The nature of each question is obvious. A mutual exchange of kisses during sexual preliminaries and through-out actual connection is one of the most reliable symptoms of a woman's desire and ability to be aroused. Should she fondle the male genitals, it is a substantial indication she is, at least, not completely inhibited. The probability, therefore, is strong that a heart-to-heart talk combined with sexual tact can bring her to more complete abandon-ment.

To estimate the possibility of a successful adjustment, a husband may credit his domestic sexual future with a value of "1" for every "Yes" answer and take a deduction of "2" for every "No." This form of grading anticipates that a satisfactory readjustment at a late date depends upon every small advantage a man can obtain. Hence, "Yes" is valued with a grade of 1, because many of these counts are necessary to achieve a passing mark. Since he can afford but few debits against him, the "No" answers are extremely penalizing, and quickly add up to impos-sibility.

As far as the average woman is concerned, and she represents the majority, a man cannot answer questions 1 through 4 with the answer "No" and expect all responses to questions 9 through 12 to be affirmative. The average woman will eventually sense her husband's true feelings and set up defenses of her own. Consequently, "No" in one section also begets "No" in another; that is, if a husband is not engaged in wishful thinking.

To determine his possibilities for a successful adjust-ment, a husband simply compares the totals of his "Yes" and "No" answers. If for example there are 4 "No" an-swers and 11 "Yes" answers, the relationship is 8 to 11 in favor of a more sexually compatible future. Should his tallies result in 6 "No" answers and 10 "Yes" answers, the odds favor failure by 12 to 10. Should he be so fortunate as to draw all "Yes" answers, there is no doubt of a successfull re-adjustment. If the answers 7 and 8 carry the answers "No," he may take credit for "Yes" responses provided his future relationships are conducted accordingly. Nor is there any reason why within a reasonably short time "No" answers to questions 5 and 6 may also be converted to "Yes," following the correction of whatever deficiencies exist.

It is clear that such an analysis allows few debits. On the other hand, it offers hope to the sexually disappointed husband who, given a proper outline to follow, may yet salvage many years of compatibility from a seemingly hopeless future of frustration.

17.

The Case Against Circumcision

S INCE this book is intended to serve as a layman's manual on the practical aspects of the sex act, the author feels nothing should be omitted that has a direct bearing upon the subject. Futhermore, whether it be utilized or not, it is impossible to provide a public, starving for adequate instructions, with too much information calculated to promote sexual compatibility in the home.

The remarks in this chapter will probably not have much influence on present-day American practice. They are made for what they are worth and the possibility that some future parents may think them deserving of consideration in the event of the birth of a male child. The author refers to the practice of circumcision, the disadvantages of which far outweigh any advantage.

One wonders what acute health situation led to its advocacy and makes it so often a routine operation at birth in this country. Paradoxically, a similar structure is found within the female genitals; yet no physician would recommend amputating the small lips of the vulva, which correspond to the foreskin of the penis and perform the same function of protection. Nor is circumcision of the small lips unknown. Female circumcision is practiced ritually by some African tribes. It has also been practiced by the Turks to allow the male organ easier access to the vagina. Fortunately, it has been overlooked in this country.

Of course, there are certain organs of the body that apparently serve no useful purpose and can at times cause serious harm. The most common of these are the tonsils and appendix. It is a peculiarity of these organs that they are not necessarily subject to control by careful living. Infection can occur notwithstanding the attention given to one's body.

But the same is not true of the foreskin. In fact its existence could scarcely be less related. First of all, it performs a necessary function, a function intended it by nature; second, given the most indifferent attention, it cannot possibly threaten the health of the human body. These statements do not permit any argument whatsoever.

It represents a minor hazard—at no times is it major— only to those who are unclean or neglectful. Even in these instances, the blame can be laid directly upon parents for not having trained a child to a simple observance that completely eliminates any threat. In truth, there is no more justification for routine circumcision than for mechanically extracting a youngster's teeth simply because lack of care may one day result in abcesses. At the very worst, there is always more than ample time for the removal of the foreskin, should it start giving trouble. At no stage is circumcision a serious undertaking. Its practice upon a week-old baby indicates this.

The discussion in this chapter pertains exclusively to its acceptance by gentiles. With Semitic people it has the influence of their religion behind it, and this is sufficient to justify it. The ceremony is a holy one, and has for its background the teachings of Moses. But since circumcision is no part of Christian dogma, it has been adopted by the gentile on the basis of health alone; on that basis it is challenged.

The foreskin is a sheath of flesh that is a proper and continuous part of the skin of the penis. It extends over the head or glans, precisely as a cap or hood, and prevents its coming into contact with the groin or clothing, much the same as the outer and inner lips of the female protect the vulva. The skin is snug yet sufficiently elastic to be drawn back completely exposing the head. This action occurs during intercourse.

The foreskin protects the glans from contact with rough surfaces, and enables it to retain a pronounced sensitivity. The slightest touch upon the head by anything not lubricated, even the finger, creates a sharp feeling of tenderness similar to that experienced when a piece of raw flesh is exposed.

Before circumcision, the glans is a deep pink, much as the organ of any male animal when upon erection it protrudes from its sheath. Also it is kept moist by the foreskin in the same manner that the vulva of the female is lubricated by the small lips.

The head comes to a rounded blunt point, but its base is somewhat larger than the rest of the male organ. This creates a ridge or band, as if a ring were placed around it, and which, when in contact with the vaginal canal during intercourse, produces a rippling along the walls. In fact, devices exist, known as "ticklers," that fit over the glans of undersized organs to increase stimulation of the vaginal canal.

Since the glans is larger than the section of the penis adjoining it, an encircling crevice is formed. Like any crevice it invites accumulations, and in the case of the male organ, a white deposit gathers there called *smegma*.

If allowed to accumulate for several years, smegma might possibly cause some irritation. But, even this is doubtful. It is troublesome only in connection with adhesions. However, to give advocates of circumcision the best of every possible argument, let it be assumed that a deposit of years will result in irritation. The fact is, then, smegma can gather for months without producing the slightest discomfort. The gatherings are not vast materializations of a suddenness, but slow, tiny accumulations that may or may not become larger only over a considerable period of time. Meanwhile, since a child or his parents can have removed it on a hundred different occasions, this leaves an uncircumcised adult without any excuse for its accumulation other than unpardonable uncleanliness.

Smegma is easily removed. The foreskin is simply drawn back and the area cleaned with a wash cloth. A female performs a similar operation each time she showers. In her case, though, greater difficulty is encountered, because of the many folds and convolutions of the vulva and the fact that inspection is awkward.

Actually, the only inconvenience likely to develop results from adhesions. If the foreskin is not drawn back regularly, it may grow in spots to the ridge about the head of the penis; or if not stretched, it may in rare instances bind the glans. This can only occur if an uncircumcised individual *never* draws back the foreskin over a very long period. The word "regularly" implies as seldom as once every 2 or 3 days in maturity, and then only if the boy or man is lazy, stupid, or not clean. An intelligent person, obviously, will attend to this matter frequently, perhaps upon each urination. A male spends at least fifteen seconds holding his organ, and only an instant is required to draw back the foreskin.

Under these circumstances, due to regular stretching, both binding of the glans and adhesions are not even to be considered. Perhaps, even nature, herself, anticipated carelessness on the part of man and deliberately created conditions to offset it. The glans is smooth and moist, and neither smooth nor moist surfaces encourage adhesions.

Nevertheless, let it be further assumed that the threat of adhesion is far more serious than it actually is and that the ridge of the glans and the foreskin will eventually grow together. Since the actual condition is one to discourage this, the surfaces at worst can adhere only in spots. Smegma then accumulates in the crevices below the ridge of the glans and beneath the adhesion. There it cannot be reached and pain and irritation occur. What now? The adhesion is cut and deposit removed. Or what is more probable, the doctor, realizing he has a careless individual for a patient, will recommend a complete circumcision.

Therein lies the sole reason for routine circumcision: the neglect of a few. Male children from clean homes and clean parents are mechanically penalized because a careless minority must be protected from its own stupidity.

Notwithstanding the fact that circumcision is unnecessary, the author still would not question it but for a most unfortunate consequence. The man with a foreskin, although he does not realize it, experiences an intensity of pleasure in intercourse that does not extend to the circumcised. Let this be clarified.

It must be admitted that nature makes few mistakes, considerably less than man, and she definitely intended the foreskin. Sound, specific, and clever functions were provided for it and those functions it performs. So long as it does, mechanical removal cannot be justified.

The functions of the foreskin are two in number. The first is to protect the head of the penis and keep in sensitive. Why? Because the nerve center of sexual sensation in the male lies at the base of the head of the penis and no-where else. It requires greater protection than the clitoris of the female, to which it corresponds, because in many women other parts of the vulva may be almost equally sensitive.

This is not the case with the male organ. The sensation of climax starts only at the head and develops its intensity there. Who, then, will insist that nature intended that particular zone to be desensitized unnecessarily?

Certainly, if the ovaries become infected, a hysterectomy must be performed to protect health. If a leg becomes gangrenous, it must be amputated for the same reason. But for what intelligent consideration does one mechanically remove an organ, limb, or section of the human body so long as the part is performing an important role in life and is not menacing health.

It has been remarked that before circumcision the head of the penis is pink, and tender to the touch. Following the operation it rapidly becomes greyish and so insensitive that sandpaper can be rubbed against it without creating the slightest pain. Since circumcision exposes the bare glans by necessitating the amputation of all the protective skin, constant contact, then, with clothing quickly reduces its sensitivity to that of ordinary epidermis. This is the effect of circumcision upon the sexual center of the male body.

The second function performed by the foreskin is an ingenious one. It acts as a natural "tickler," a contrivance referred to earlier, and adds to the stimulation of the female by increasing the circumference of the male organ. Since the foreskin is a loose section of flesh surrounding the head of the glans, the forward motion of the penis in the vaginal canal during intercourse forces the foreskin back automatically and causes it to bunch in folds at the base of the head. The withdrawing motion then reverses the operation. The clinging contact of the foreskin to the vaginal walls causes it to be drawn forward, and again cover the head of the penis, increasing its size.

It should be mentioned that the vaginal walls are in many cases extremely sensitive and will respond to any variation of pressure against them. It is the rippling of the walls brought about by the ridge of the glans that produces the highest ecstasy in a passionate woman. So susceptible are vaginal walls to stimulation that the pulsing of the penis alone, as it expands and contracts, can induce an orgasm in many women, or heighten a climax already in progress. During a female orgasm, the vagina, likewise, expands and contracts as if attempting to crowd itself more snugly about the male organ. This gripping sensation can be felt by the penis.

Consequently any variations of pressure against the walls, regardless of how slight, registers directly and immediately upon the sexual mechanism of the female and intensifies her pleasure. This function the foreskin performs by increasing the head circumference upon one motion and decreasing it upon another. Furthermore, since the thrust of the penis drives the foreskin back to bunch itself at the base of the head, it tends to thicken the ridge. This also varies the pressure against the vaginal walls.

It becomes clear then that the foreskin in addition to playing a protective role also serves as an important instrument in varying the sensations experienced by the female during intercourse.

Its amputation, therefore, actually reduces the circumference of the penis, by more than $\frac{1}{16}$ of an inch, and sentences it to perform in an unvarying manner. Since the vaginal walls will respond violently to the even more minute momentary increase in size brought about alone by a pulsation of the penis, $\frac{1}{16}$ of an inch is a large measurement by comparison.

To future parents of male children, it is suggested that they weigh the matter very carefully before exposing a boy to a mechanical operation that has no better recommendation that the argument that *some* people are unclean and neglectful. The questionable gain does not at all compensate for the unnecessary loss. It must be emphasized again that since sexual incompatibility constitutes such a threat to domestic happiness, a man requires every support he can obtain to meet it. Circumcision will not aid him.

18.

Sexual Miscellany

CHAPTER 15 contained a discussion of the eventual decline of the average woman's desire for sexual intercourse. The subject matter of this chapter deals rather with early aversions brought about by some specific known or unknown happening. Reference has been made to the possibility of a woman's developing sexual restraint because of the proximity in girlhood of her bedroom to that of her parents—not a typical situation, however. Nonetheless, too many women are disinclined to engage in intercourse as frequently as their husbands wish, however reasonable the men may be in their demands.

If this condition exists, then the husband is faced with a grave problem, and his wife with a still more serious one; she risks losing him to another woman, and it will not be entirely his fault. However, since few women realize this until too late, it is best for husbands to avoid the possibility by attacking it at the beginning, at the wife's very first manifestation of excessive aloofness to intercourse. This is the sole responsibility of the husband; the wife can do nothing to assist except express herself, which she probably will not do.

If the husband's marital sexual behavior has not created this distaste for intimacy in his wife or if there is no serious *general* incompatibility, then only a few conclusions are possible: either she is not experiencing the orgasm; she is not being thoroughly satisfied; the sex act is painful; her husband no longer physically attracts her; she suspects him of philandering; she has developed some mental quirk with respect to intercourse, subsequent to her marriage; or some conception of pre-marital existence has asserted a greater influence than she believed possible.

If the husband is constant, one possibility is eliminated; another, if she admits intercourse is not painful; and a third if she has not fallen out of love.

While good sex relationship cements, preserves, and adds balance to domestic life, there are women who can be constant and devoted wives and never experience the desire for intimacy. They are, of course, completely frigid, at least as far as their husbands are concerned. They can feel every other emotion—admiration, respect, appreciation, affection, to mention a few—for their husbands, but not physical desire.

However, if the wife is still in love with her husband, only common possibilities remain for consideration. They may be regarded in this fashion: since the husband knows that prior to marriage his wife was normally responsive to love-making, barring the intercourse which may or may not have taken place, he knows also that she did feel some physical attraction for him, and that his caresses were not disagreeable to her. This makes it clear either that the girl was not frigid or else was a capable actress, which is unlikely; no woman can affect a convincing display of sexual affection over a long period of time. It is reasonable to assume, then, that she found him physically appealing when she married him.

Consequently, the fault must lie in the intercourse or in

some pre-marital or post-marital concepts concerning it; it is up to the husband to determine which.

The first move a psychiatrist makes toward destroying a phobia is to discover its origin. Having succeeded, he next tries to make the patient realize that it is a phobia. Also, a psychiatrist will admit that improvement begins when he gains the patient's confidence. In sex life, more than any other type of association, every husband must practice psychology, and psychiatry to the extent of determining the nature of his wife's sexual inhibitions, if any. As her husband, he already has the advantage of her confidence. If he hasn't, he must gain it.

Gaining a wife's confidence with respect to sexual behavior is not the easy task it might seem. In fact, it is a most difficult one. Frequently, regardless of how much a husband may try to convince his partner that certain forms of indulgence are perfectly proper, she will fail to be reassured.

One of the greatest mistakes a husband makes is in not realizing this. He assumes a wife will take anything he says for granted simply because he is her husband. However, no woman will accept a man's bare word for the propriety of a sexual behavior that she has always regarded doubtfully, unless she has complete confidence in his sexual knowledge. The thought persists that he may be fitting his explanations to suit his personal desires; that such desires are peculiar, perhaps, only to him. It is well to add, also, for the benefit of the male that the casual approach to sex is not only the sophisticated way of dealing with the matter, but is also the most effective means of establishing confidence in a woman. Consequently, when a wife sees that a husband regards intimacy with a matter-of-fact attitude, that everything which takes place is performed with the same unselfconsciousness that characterizes eating breakfast, she is more inclined to accept sex at its face value.

Unfortunately, when a woman is sexually aloof, most men try to attack the problem in bed, the one place which should be avoided. They attempt to force, persist, argue, and bully their way through a purely mental obstacle. Their unreasonable and lustful attitude intensifies the woman's distaste for something which is proving to be precisely what she regards it—disagreeable. She acquires a dread of bedtime and its customary interval of bickering. She affects headaches, pretends she wants to sit up and read, throws out a hint that she is unusually tired, and invents a hundred and one devices to postpone the inevitable moment. If through sheer weariness, she finally submits, the husband has accomplished nothing but the satisfaction of his own desire and the intensification of the irritation which disturbs his wife.

It is obvious also that whatever must be done cannot be effected overnight. The husband must be prepared to expend time and patience in the destruction of a mental block, if it is only that. Failing in this, he must rely upon whatever professional services are available or be forced to look elsewhere for a suitable mate. However, he should make every possible effort to solve the problem before abandoning it.

Since the husband knows that, before marriage, his wife was affectionate and not averse to conventional caresses, he can at least regard the situation as hopeful. Also, since the process of elimination indicates that the trouble lies in the intercourse or pre- or post-marital ideas concerning it, he has definitely limited the field of consideration. And since the final analysis suggests that whatever the reason, intercourse is disagreeable, he must determine why. As long as he fails to do this, the situation will not improve.

Obviously, as a previous chapter advised, the logical approach is a direct and frank discussion wherein the wife is asked specifically what phase of sexual relation is repugnant to her and why. This she can certainly explain, but she may be evasive for fear of hurting her husband. Therefore, he must be prepared to bring out the answers and hear revelations possibly embarrassing to him.

For one thing, his breath may be bad, a fact which he does not realize; he may be careless with respect to body odor; he may engage in distasteful practices; he may wish to indulge too frequently; he may leave his wife unsatisfied; he may neglect foreplay. These are only a few of the possibilities for which he himself may be directly at fault.

On the other hand, none of these factors may present the difficulty. The wife may know only that the sex act in general is disagreeable. Even so, she can explain to what extent. Perhaps, she finds it sordid and an affront to her modesty. At least, her husband has now isolated the cause. Although he may not know what lies behind the aversion, he knows it is purely mental.

Since he has determined that intercourse is disagreeable to her, he undertakes to make it agreeable. If the barrier is physical, it is the more easily removed. The real problem exists when the aversion is mental. Should he be able to discover that his wife's coldness has its seat in the past, his approach must take this into consideration.

Assume, for example, that when she was a girl her parents engaged in constant sexual squabbling; it is clear that her husband must refrain from such practice if he is not to aggravate her aloofness. He must also intrude as little of himself as possible into each intimacy. In a perfectly natural and relevant manner, he can implant from time to time some thought that he wants to register. This he does prior to bedtime to give his wife opportunity to turn it over in her mind. He might avoid the bedroom altogether as the scene of intimacy; it may arouse unpleasant memories in her. Whatever the procedure, its success depends almost entirely upon his approach.

It must be emphasized that a woman, particularly the lowly and moderately sensitive, will rarely complain or volunteer information in connection with sexual activity. She will tell a man that she does not like his suit, his tie, his disposition, his untidiness, his attitude, his behavior, his initiative, or a hundred other things all of a purely personal and intimate character. But some unaccountable modesty will prevent her from complaining about, or even discussing, a condition regarding which the greatest frankness of all is necessary—his sexual association with her.

Man, himself, is to a limited extent also a victim of this false modesty, but not nearly to the same degree as woman. Regardless of his general ignorance, he is by comparison more informed than the female, though it be only through hearsay. A woman assumes he is more experienced and usually looks to him for initial instruction. What he suggests or prefers in the early stages of marriage she accepts and allows to become a habit, unless it conflicts too sharply with her established, preconceived ideas. She regards their activity as a standard procedure probably existent in every home. He is a man, and she believes he should know. If she subsequently discovers certain elements are in opposition to her emotions, she is inclined to believe that she, rather than the system, is at fault. Her desires, she feels, may be out of proportion to what is usual, and she does not wish to shock her husband. He seems to be perfectly satisfied with the game as everyone is playing it. Consequently, she maintains patience until a point of saturation is reached.

Unfortunately, she does not know that millions of women stand precisely on the same ground: that they have drawn her conclusions and are likewise maintaining silence. The result is that sooner or later this group decides that sex is a highly over-rated activity. In the end, they look upon it as an obligation, and, when pressed, submit to it passively, mechanically, and unenthusiastically. To their husbands they are cold.

If a woman is married to a man in all other respects perfectly adequate, there is no reason why he should not just as adequately satisfy her sexually. If he fails, something is wrong; no woman can avoid enjoying sexual intimacy if it is properly conducted and she loves her husband. Nine times out of ten, the fault will lie with the male, but he will fail to realize it unless he is told.

It is true that desire tapers off gradually the longer a couple is married. However, at those rarer intervals when the inclination does assert itself, there is no reason why it should lack appeal any more for one than for the other. Nor will it, if the couple has always maintained satisfactory sexual relationships. Should it do so, it is only because a flaw has always existed.

When a couple have not grown tired of each other—there is nothing to be done when that stage is reached—most discontent may be attributed to false modesty. This is a deadly quality and, as has been said, imposes a firm barrier to the complete abandon necessary to perfect sexual association. In connection with normal sex, an invisible legend should hang in every bedchamber in the country: "Nothing Done in Bed Is Wrong." If every reader would implant that statement firmly in his or her mind and accept it, regardless of how far his desires may impel him, the sexual intimacy of man and woman would be vastly improved. It should always be borne in mind that millions of people are doing everything the reader does or would like to do.

There is nothing indecent about the nude human body; it is only one's thoughts which make it so. The penis is no less an organ than an arm or a leg, and a woman's breast no more unusual than the buttocks exposed in a brief swimming suit. Today, a reproduction of "September Morn" arouses hardly a flash of interest. We are accustomed to it.

Nudism is not an intelligent practice, nor is it advocated. However impracticable, it can scarcely be criticized on the ground that exposure of the private organs constitutes an indecency. As long as many people regard these organs as such, so long will they experience a guilt reaction every time these organs are utilized for any purpose other than tending to necessary wants. This develops inhibitions, and there should be none between sexual partners.

The artist looks at his nude model with a mind far removed from the pubic region. He sees only those organs which he wishes to paint. The obstetrician probes, and the surgeon removes an ovary, without becoming sexually aroused. Their minds are clean, and all see the human body for what it is—an assortment of organs. Others look at it and see only indecency. Let them examine their minds.

Europe is a continent where an American can feel very uncomfortable in the beginning but perfectly at home after he adjusts himself. It may take a little time for an American tourist to become used to the experience of finding female attendants in some men's lavatories. Street-corner urinals may embarrass his wife and daughter, but the native pays no attention to them. Tending to one's wants is as natural to him as nature intended it to be. Of course, we Americans prefer our own habits not only because we are accustomed to them but also because we see no reason to emphasize unnecessarily purely private functions. But, having become exposed to these other environments, it is not difficult for a person to adjust himself once he realizes that it is the order of another world.

With respect to sex, the European is just as informal. He regards it as a perfectly normal function, as a routine practice. The attitude toward love is as philosophical as the resignation to war. *"C'est l'amour"* is uttered with the same imperturbability as *"C'est la guerre."*

Between couples, it must be remembered that one or both may be sexually responsive either in a manner not within the previous experience of the other, or not corresponding to adolescent conceptions. Consequently, when a wife in her adult life begins to experience sexual desires which do not fall within her previous concepts, she may conclude that she is outside the normal sphere and must maintain a check upon her impulses.

Her husband, on the other hand, may hold a similar belief regarding himself. Thus, two people continue to practice only conventional sex. Each hopes the other will manifest some tendency to engage otherwise; each wonders if he dare take the initiative and risk being misunderstood. This is unfortunate, particularly when a knowledge of what is actually taking place between millions of couples would assure one or the other, or both, that their desires are perefectly normal and constitute proper sex practice.

How, then, should a woman go about expressing her

inhibited desires to a man whose response may be a state of outraged morals? If he never takes the initiative, it is best for her to do so. The probabilities are almost entirely in her favor that she will not shock him but will behave in a manner which he himself has been wondering secretly how to bring about. The same applies to the male, but he also runs little risk even should the woman be extremely reserved in her habits. Under normal circumstances, she will be inclined to mark it down as a general masculine tendency and not an exclusive habit of her husband.

With respect to second marriages, a great danger exists in the fact that those who engage in it may be sexually disappointed in the new. The first partner may have been highly passionate, and the second decidedly passive. This is unfortunate, and there is nothing to be done except to attempt to develop the sexual possibilities of the woman. However, a man's sexual disposition cannot be altered. A passionate woman is therefore faced with the greater problem if her newly acquired mate does not measure up to her demands. Since a man is capable of gratification with any type of woman, his situation is less disturbing. Though he might enjoy a more active partner, his discontent lies only in the degree of his enjoyment, not in his ultimate gratification; a woman can be affected in both respects.

It might seem, then, that the most fortunate combination would be both a woman and man without any previous sexual experience whatever. It might seem that each could enjoy the other, unimpeded by a knowledge that a still more suitable partner for either of them might exist. However, even that situation may not work out too well. It would be satisfactory for the husband, but his ignorance might not enable him adequately to handle a wife whose emotional level might be very high. Incompatibility could result in any case.

Regardless of conditions, sexual incompatibility is always a threat. That it is so in fact is testified to by the tremendous amount of existing sexual dissatisfaction. Occasionally, two people of perfectly complementary sexual natures unite. It is rare, and they frequently fail to appreciate their good fortune. Generally, however, sexual harmony is a grab-bag affair, a blind article which can turn out to be anything once the couple are wed.

Actually, the most desirable situation presents a thoroughly seasoned male with the capacity to adjust himself to whatever sexual temperament he may find in his wife and the ability to develop her as far as her possibilities will allow. Such an informed husband knows that the deep sexual attraction which initially draws two people together is impermanent; that general compatibility is the most important condition of all. He knows that when the physical desire dwindles, as it is certain to do, there must be something more than the body to hold two people together; he therefore strives only for the balance which good sexual association will impart to the marriage. No happy state of wedlock can exist permanently when it is based solely on a sexual foundation. While the spiritual and mental factors are far more important than the physical, it is unfortunate, nevertheless, that regardless of the importance of the other materials, the entire matrimonial structure may topple unless bound together with sound, sexual ribs. It is not the writer's purpose to elevate sex beyond its importance, but to emphasize its actual value as a primary factor in keeping the marriage together.

Intelligent people will accept nature's impulses for what they are and respond to them in whatever manner gives them pleasure, whether or not it coincides with their pre-conceived notions of conventional sex. After all, what is conventional sex? It is true that society may determine convention, but no individual group has been elected to do so or has been designated as arbiter of the public taste. Many try to usurp the position, but they may be disregarded. Consequently, there is nothing conventional about sex, because no one has the authority to set a fashion for it.

False modesty touches both sexes, but is largely confined to the female. The assumption of every husband should be that his wife is to some extent a victim of it. He should, therefore, take the initiative, and make a studied effort to insure the fact that his mate enters into intimacy with complete abandon. In fact, the thoughtful husband, whatever his mood, will be alert to anticipate his wife's feelings. Since the average woman is reluctant to make passionate advances, she waits for him to take the initiative; frequently she waits in vain. On the other hand, a dutiful and considerate wife, unless she is indisposed, tired out, or mentally upset, should be equally solicitous; this assumes, of course, that no abnormal circumstances exist.

The female has very definite duties apart from her obligation to render normal sexual service to her husband. She must remember that, while there are certain regular periods in which intercourse is neither practicable nor convenient, her husband may nevertheless require sexual relief. Should her period run five, six, seven, or eight days, this is a lengthy interval for the male to practice self-control. Of course, he should be able to do it, but there is no reason to force it upon him when the simple expedient of the female hand or oral connection can remove the necessity. Since many men are reluctant to force any type of relationship upon their wives during this period, the woman herself should take the initiative. Furthermore, in all probability this variation will prove enjoyable to him and will be just as satisfying. A thoughtful wife will, independently, look for these opportunities to gratify her husband's sexual needs. It is true that she deserves first consideration, but not the only consideration. It might be added, also, that in conducting sexual intimacy, it is equally the duty of the wife to excite her partner by engaging in genital stimulation. The woman who lies passively and overlooks these essentials is as guilty of neglect in her way as the husband who fails to satisfy her. Sex in marriage is not a one-sided matter. If excessive modesty or aloofness tends to make it so, a wife had better adjust her conceptions; otherwise, she may find her husband seeking the society of a more suitable mistress.

The male is usually direct in indicating his feelings. When his hands start moving over the female body, a wife instantly recognizes in this a symptom of his mood. Nevertheless, although they also are entitled to similar liberties, and should not hesitate to stimulate the male organ as an expression of their mood, few women will release their inhibitions to this extent. When they do, however, the greatest degree of sexual compatibility usually exists, because they feed the male ego and the partner is made to realize that he still has the ability to attract his wife physically. As a result, an understanding of some nature should definitely be arranged.

Many newly wed men, instead of proceeding leisurely, are impatient to run the gamut of sex in the first few relationships. One can well understand the reaction of a woman who, on the second night of intimacy with her husband, finds him experimenting with the rear-entry position, the conception of which may be completely new to her. If she assumes that he is utilizing her as a mechanism to satisfy jaded tastes or as a medium of experiment, she can hardly be blamed, particularly if she is uninformed. Virgins have been known to burst into tears when their husbands first attempted this position, and accuse the men of lacking respect for them. Obviously these women are naive. Nevertheless, a man should consider these possibilities; there is no excuse for haste. Naturally, an informed woman will regard the varying of a position as a perfectly common procedure; even an uninformed bride will consider it in the same light, given time for adjustment.

A woman who insists upon practicing sexual activity exclusively in the dark or beneath the covers is, indeed, overdoing the matter of modesty. This is the sign of an immature conception of sex and an indication of an inhibited nature. This is bad not only for the individual so constituted but for the partner as well; it eliminates, too, an element very necessary to sexual relationship: variety. Indulgence conducted in the light has the capacity also to heighten the excitement of the male; it gives him the opportunity of viewing the physical charms of his wife. However, they should be casually observed and not gloated over.

There is an old axiom, the substance of which is that the perfect wife is a lady in the drawing room, a capable cook in the kitchen, and a wanton in bed. There is much truth in this. Many a prostitute can satisfy a man more completely than a virtuous woman; she is a mistress of sexual technique, knows masculine psychology, and has no inhibitions. Having consorted with all types, she understands their sexual natures thoroughly and conducts herself accordingly. This appeals to most men. The wife who abandons herself will be looked upon by an intelligent husband as simply behaving like a woman. By so doing, she adds to his pleasure as well as to her own. If a woman will bear in mind that there is nothing she can do in bed that is not being done in this country and throughout the world by women every bit as respectable, she cannot regard herself as an exception in a sexual universe.

However, it is easily understood why wives who have never experienced the orgasm, may be sexually indifferent. Passivity for them is a natural state. Many such wives are mistakenly regarded by their husbands as being cold. Actually, the fault lies in the ignorance of their male partners who do not recognize the absence of a climax in their wives during intercourse. Obviously, no amount of discussion can remove such a woman's inhibitions. She has no sexual responses to appeal to and, therefore, finds no reason to alter her previous conceptions. To her, intercourse is a disappointment and respresents nothing but an indecent coupling of the bodies. Had she been at all informed, the absence of any unusual emotion or the disappointing unfullfilment of her desires might have aroused her suspicions to the point where she would have talked over the matter with her husband. Obviously, such a wife must become accustomed to the climax before a discussion stage can be considered. Even then, the problem still remains of removing inhibitions seriously ingrown during her years of passivity. If, however, her sensations of orgasm are sufficiently overwhelming, this new experience may offset the time factor and encourage a satisfactory re-adjustment.

Removing these mental blocks to a point where a wife may eventually enter into complete abandonment sexually, involves patience and persistence. Situations may exist, however, where for some subconscious reason, having its existence deep in the past, a woman may not be able to unharness her restraints. This condition calls for psychotherapy, a treatment that can consume a lengthy period of time and a substantial amount of money. However, it is possible to attack the problem in a similar manner, but one less complex, less expensive, and more frequently than not, one that produces speedier results. It is not at all a new science. In fact it is as old, if not older, than modern psychiatry as fathered by Freud. Furthermore, it is beginning to occupy a prominent position in the scientific field. Many people, suffering from mental disturbances of various types, have been successfully treated by this advancing medium of *hypnotherapy,* which has a characteristic advantage of reaching the root of an established ailment with surprising speed. Because under hypnosis the patient is more or less unaware of his responses, he will answer questions and unburden himself with less hesitancy and greater frankness than under any similar form of questioning. Hypnosis directly touches the sub-conscious mind wherein lie our forgotten experiences and suppressions.

For this reason, costly sittings and tedious sessions, in which the patient *consciously* attempts to probe his memory for unremembered incidents, are eliminated. So far as the sub-conscious is concerned, our total experience is impressed there. Little, if anything is forgotten by it, and hypnosis releases this stream of data directly to the operator.

No one need fear hypnotism when practiced by an ethical member of the medical profession, of whom there are many and of steadily increasing number. One day posterity will look back on us with wonderment at our failure to utilize its almost miraculous possibilities.

A few facts with respect to hypnosis will dissipate much of the mistrust surrounding it, mistrust born of old wives' tales and misinformation.

Firstly, no hypnotist can force a subject to commit any act to which the subject would be opposed in a conscious state.

Secondly, no subject can be hypnotized against his will. His full cooperation is essential.

Thirdly, a capable hypnotist can function effectively before witnesses. In the matter under discussion, a husband need not be barred. In fact, his presence could be desirable.

Fourthly, the subject will awaken even though the command to do so may not be given by the hypnotist.

The first reaction of the layman to the word "hypnotism" is the thought that, like Svengali's Trilby, he can become the slave of the hypnotist. With women, their minds immediately turn to the sexual helplessness hypnotism may induce. Lastly, of course, is the fear of not awakening. None of these are causes for alarm.

Without going into a discussion of hypnotism, beyond its relationship to sexual problems it is recommended that a couple who may be considering this form of therapy, visit a reliable *medical* practitioner of the science. A professional man who has not studied hypnotism is hardly a person to consult. In fact, he is likely to know less about it than an intelligent layman.

Since a man is inclined to be thoughtless with respect to his sexual duties, his wife, as has been said, is entitled to make her desires known. However, if after reading these pages, she is still reluctant—as many may be—to approach the matter directly, there is an indirect method of arousing a sluggish male. It must be employed carefully, casually, and with seeming innocence if it is not to lose its illusion.

A wife should realize that all normal men are sexually responsive to the exposure of the female body. This is particularly true where strange women are concerned, since the male perpetually seeks variety. It accounts for the popularity of burlesque and girl shows in general, and for exhibitions of the "strip-tease," bubble-dance, and fan-dance character. Few husbands, if any, are totally indifferent to these attractions.

At the same time, they are also susceptible to stimulation where a parallel situation arises with their wives. For example, a stockinged leg exposed to the thigh has eye appeal for any man even though his wife may be the possessor. A wife attired in brief lingerie has as much opportunity to arouse interest in an apathetic male as the scantily clad chorines in a present-day musical. A negligée, carelessly draped to provide an occasional glimpse of what lies beneath it, will succeed in stimulating male desire where absolute nudity fails completely. A sheer nightgown whose transparency outlines the female body has greater seductive value than one of coarser fabric; otherwise a woman may just as well wear a house dress to bed. In fact, any indirect exposure which would stimulate a man if observed on another woman has a comparable effect when provided by his wife; perhaps not in the same degree, but sufficiently extensive to make him desire her. It is up to the wife to sense these opportunities and utilize them subtly. Nudity is not effective when paraded.

It must be borne in mind that there is more to sex than intercourse, although many minds rush to dwell only on that phase. Sex is comprised of numerous small and incidental habits, such as the use of an enticing perfume, a well-fitted brassiere, a tight stocking with the seam running straight up the back, a high-heeled slipper—not a shapeless flat-heeled moccasin or ballet pump—to lend grace to the leg, instep, and ankle, a clean house dress, unsmeared lipstick. These and numerous other small and unneglected considerations are what keep a wife sexually desirable to her husband and lead to frequency of sexual intimacy, not merely periodic occurrence. It should be added that keeping sex vitally alive in the marriage is a constant engagement against the forces of familiarity and consequent indifference that follow. It is as important as the struggle of a woman to maintain her figure, delay the wrinkles, and control her weight, a struggle which needs every possible ally.

Since sex will not automatically retain its original vigor, a couple cannot overdo their attempts to keep it active. In this respect, one of the most important nutrients to sex life is variety, and it should be introduced at every opportunity. By variety is not meant change of position exclusively, but change in environment or locale, even though it be in the same apartment.

The sex life of the average couple is a deadly routine gone through with a monotonous sameness, the same position in the same bed at the same time in the same way. There is no reason why matrimony need interrupt all the pre-marital habits of a wedded couple. An occasional drive to the haunts of yesteryear and a petting party to recapture a measure of the old-time magic should not strike the married reader as a preposterous suggestion. Neither should a weekend spent at a modest farm or an occasional night at a hotel. If one cannot afford a periodic vacation or does not own a car, there are always alternatives to the familiar bed. Anything which breaks the monotony of sameness is desirable.

These are the identical procedures in which a man engages with his sweetheart, in which a man at any age engages with any woman excepting, unfortunately, his wife. If a husband feels too old and mature for such romantic nonsense, then let him remember that his wife never does. Actually, neither does he. Let him become smitten with an attachment twenty years his junior, and he will discover it also.

It is appropriate to discuss in this section a piece of folly characteristic of both sexes, especially the female. It will never result in the slightest bit of good, and it always has the power to inflict serious harm. This menace consists of voluntary confessions of pre-marital and post-marital "affairs." The former, in particular, are the more unnecessary and, of course, the more numerous, although a guilty conscience has driven many a woman to confess to the latter. Notwithstanding its utter stupidity, this honesty indicates, nevertheless, a strong sense of innate though misguided decency which in itself should be powerful enough to bring about complete forgiveness. Unfortunately it often fails to receive the full consideration it deserves.

Never was a platitude more fitting to a circumstance than the one applying in this instance, "What you don't know, won't bother you," and only a person who is determined to tamper with future happiness will ignore it.

A woman, in particular, should never voluntarily confess indiscretions to her husband unless blackmailed. At that time, there is no other sane course to take but confess and prepare to accept the consequences. Regardless of what happens, she will be more secure in the long run than undergoing the consistent mental torture inflicted by an extortioner. In all probability, it will result in exposure anyway. If a husband is not the type to forgive isolated infidelity, then he is neither deep nor generous, and the woman is better off without him. Some men will forgive, others will not, but it is regrettable that few, if any, will forget.

It does no harm and may even do good if the prospective husband should hint at the fact that he has sown wild oats, provided he really has. Most women expect this in a male. However, one or two pre-marital sex relationships hardly make a man of experience; it requires considerably more before he can know how adequately to handle even his wife.

But should he actually have some background of experience, the suggestion of it to his prospective bride will allow her to take some confidence from the fact that he will be at least an informed lover. This is quite heartening, particularly where the female is actually innocent and consequently ignorant of sex and its ramifications.

It by no means follows, however, that the voluntary confession of post-marital philanderings is helpful in any degree. It simply means that the husband will plant in his wife's mind unnecessary doubt regarding his behavior at all times, even during required and innocent absences. This will result in coldness and definite unhappiness for her.

With respect to a woman's voluntary admissions of pre-marital experiences, even though the average man should at this date expect them to be the rule rather than the exception, nothing at all is to be gained. At the least, it is likely to remove the edge from her husband's enjoyment, since most men want to believe that their wives were intact even if they must delude themselves into thinking so. Furthermore, the husband can develop uneasiness since, if he is a novice, as many men are, he constantly wonders how he may be comparing with a predecessor. If for obvious reasons he knows that he has not been the only man, as in the case of his marrying a divorcee or widow, the bride should bolster his ego by making him believe he is by far the most proficient lover, even if she must stretch the truth. Should she find him inadequate, her previous experience should enable her to lead him tactfully in the right direction so far as she herself knows it.

It has been said that a clever woman with favorable structural conditions can delude a man into believing that she is a virgin. In the event this is impossible by reason of the fact that entrance is completely painless and immediate, there is no need for her to confess, if pressed, to more than one affair of long duration. And she is unwise if she admits to more; one of length could as readily have created the existing condition as could a prior marriage. Naturally, if a husband asks no questions, which is highly improbable, it is far better to let the matter rest and never refer to it.

However, should a woman ever voluntarily confess to infidelity, she can prepare herself for almost an absolute certainty: never again will she enjoy her husband's trust. He may forgive her, but no matter how broad-minded he may be, he will always wonder, always doubt. A woman who creates this unnecessary condition has behaved stupidly, no matter how lofty her motive. Although that one dereliction may always remain the only one, the husband will never feel certain. Men, irrespective of their own digressions, look for strict fidelity in their wives.

While it is urged that the practice of confessing voluntarily to infidelity is unwise, the advice concerns only those who are not habitual in this respect, whose lapses have been limited. The perpetually philandering husband or wife of similar bent need take nothing said in this connection as encouragement for such activities. Under any circumstances, it is only a question of time before day-after-day inconstancy is discovered.

Deceit, if deceit this be, is for the best. There may also be children, upon whose innocent heads the stupidities of the parents fall. A happy and successful marriage maintained by some slight deceit, is far more to be advocated than eventual divorce brought about by complete frankness. Only the naive or hopelessly dull can believe that "confession," with matrimony hanging in the balance, "is good for the soul."